Modern Methods of Constr
Innovative Materials

This new textbook has two main themes. The first is Modern Methods of Construction (MMC) which is the off-site manufacture of a wide spectrum of products, ranging from whole buildings to be transported onto site, down to smaller units or components for site integration. The second theme describes the innovation and progress towards carbon zero by the major generators of CO_2 in the construction industry – namely cement, steel and masonry.

The first section of the book describes and illustrates with photographs, the major forms of Modern Methods of Construction. These include fully completed 3D units, panelised systems, pods, sub-assemblies and on-site MMC. The section on Innovative Materials then describes a wide range of construction products which are entering into the built environment sector. Some new entrants are variants of well-established construction materials such as steel and concrete. Materials such as these will remain major construction materials for the foreseeable future, but their composition and manufacturing processes will inevitably have to change. Timber also will remain a major construction material, but sustainable sourcing is key and its utilisation as cross-lamination timber (CLT) or as modified timber is rapidly developing. As a result, students and practitioners must familiarise themselves with these materials, their composition, and various uses.

The book goes on to describe variants of other traditional building products, such as glass, plastic and insulation, which are undergoing major developments leading towards enhanced environmental sustainability, as well as many emergent materials, some of which are likely to be significant in future. *Modern Methods of Construction and Innovative Materials* is the only book combining these important elements of the future of the industry in an easy-to-read guide for students and new practitioners. It is essential reading for anyone studying and working in the built environment, be they architects, construction managers, surveyors or engineers.

Arthur Lyons studied science at Trinity Hall Cambridge, Warwick and Leicester Universities and has a postgraduate diploma in architectural building conservation. Lyons was honoured with life membership of the Leicestershire and Rutland Society of Architects. Since retiring from teaching in the School of Architecture of De Montfort University, Leicester, where he is an honorary research fellow, he has authored several books on construction materials including *Materials for Architects and Builders*, now in its sixth edition.

Modern Methods of Construction and Innovative Materials

Arthur Lyons

Routledge
Taylor & Francis Group

LONDON AND NEW YORK

Designed cover image: Clockwise from top left:
Crane lifting timber volumetric module for installation on building site. Copyright: Getty Images.
University of Leicester Freemen's Common Student Village. Two of the seven residential blocks incorporated significant MMC techniques including the use of prefabricated insulated sandwich panels with integral brick facing and acid-etched finishes together with factory fitted windows. Photograph: Arthur Lyons.
Installation of off-site manufactured cold-rolled steel panels in London. Photograph: Courtesy of Hiltongrove and Hamza Kadeen.
Woodolex® flexible wooden board manufactured from 96% recycled wood and 4% adhesive. Photograph: Arthur Lyons.
Modern timber construction. Copyright: Getty Images.

First published 2024
by Routledge
4 Park Square, Milton Park, Abingdon, Oxon OX14 4RN

and by Routledge
605 Third Avenue, New York, NY 10158

Routledge is an imprint of the Taylor & Francis Group, an informa business

© 2024 Arthur Lyons

British Library Cataloguing-in-Publication Data
A catalogue record for this book is available from the British Library

ISBN: 978-1-032-41934-3 (hbk)
ISBN: 978-1-032-41482-9 (pbk)
ISBN: 978-1-003-36046-9 (ebk)

DOI: 10.1201/9781003360469

Typeset in Adobe Caslon
by MPS Limited, Dehradun

Contents

About the Author

Dr Arthur Lyons, the author of many texts on building materials, was formerly Head of Quality, Principal Lecturer and Teacher Fellow for construction materials in the Leicester School of Architecture, Faculty of Arts, Design and Humanities, De Montfort University, Leicester, UK. He was educated at Trinity Hall Cambridge, Warwick and Leicester Universities in the fields of natural sciences and polymer science and has a postgraduate diploma in architectural building conservation. He was a lecturer in building materials within schools of architecture and surveying for 35 years. In recognition of his services to architects and architecture, Lyons was honoured with life membership of the local society of architects and he is a Fellow of the Higher Education Academy. He retains his active interest in architecture through liaison with the Leicestershire and Rutland Society of Architects and the Leicester School of Architecture of De Montfort University, where he is an Honorary Research Fellow. Lyons is the author of *Materials for Architects and Builders* which is now in its sixth edition (2020) with Routledge. In addition to this entirely new text, Lyons has written chapters in the *ICE Manual of Construction Materials* (2009, Institution of Civil Engineers), the *Metric Handbook: Planning and Design Data* (7th edition, 2022, Routledge) and the *Construction Materials Reference Book* (2013, Routledge). Lyons also authored four editions of *The Architecture of the Universities of Leicester*, published by AnchorPrint, and he has published a home emergency booklet, *Home Information: Help! Where do I turn it off?* Details are on the website www.arthurlyons.net.

Arthur Lyons is married to Susan. They have two daughters with families, Claire lives in Perth Australia and Elizabeth in London.

Preface

This entirely new text describes the main types of Modern Methods of Construction (MMC), and also a wide range of emerging new materials in building construction. Some of the innovations such as Cross Laminated Timber (CLT) are already well bedded into construction, but other developments, such as straw bale construction are still prototypical, and inevitably only some will be taken up by the industry, while others will prove neither successful nor economically viable. However, many are included in the text as it is not possible to predict which innovations will ultimately gain acceptance, and all options should remain open to be available to potential specifiers and users. Who would have predicted a few years ago, when first created, that graphene would have become incorporated into major building construction projects such as HS2 (High Speed 2)? The vast majority of the emerging developments have the road map to a low-carbon economy as their driving force. Fabric First is generally accepted as the key philosophy for future building followed by consideration of HEVAC (heating, ventilation and air conditioning).

It is hoped that the text will inspire future architects, builders and other built environment professionals to be creative in the materials and technologies that they specify as we move towards a zero-carbon environment. However, specifiers must always ensure that the materials they specify are appropriate to the task and comply with the regulations pertaining at the time. This text does not guarantee the viability or appropriateness of any of the materials described. Published technical data, certifications of the materials and their appropriate applications must be thoroughly checked with the manufacturers and suppliers before their use.

Acknowledgements

The author acknowledges the support of the De Montfort University library, especially in respect of access to external databases including British Standards Institution (BSI) and Construction Information Systems (CIS). The author wishes to thank Susan for her participation in the production of this book and also Claire and Elizabeth for constant support and encouragement.

The author is indebted to the numerous manufacturers of building materials and components for their trade literature and for permissions to reproduce their published data, photographs and diagrams. The author wishes to thank the building owners, architectural practices and their photographers for the inclusion of their photographs. In particular, the author wishes to thank Elaine Toogood, The Concrete Centre, London for her checking of the text relating to current and pending cement and concrete developments.

The text uses generic names for the building materials and components wherever possible. However, many of the innovative materials are so new and specific that they can only be usefully described by particular reference to their researchers, manufacturer or trade name. The specific names are therefore annotated appropriately.

I would like to thank the following organisations for giving permission to use their illustrations:

Accsys – SBM Fastwood (Fig. 12.7)
Ambient GlowTechnology – Glow Stones (Figs. 11.9 and 11.10)
Alberto Cosi / Italian Connection (Fig. 12.13)
Alusion Aluminium Foam (Fig. 13.5)
A. Proctor Group (Fig. 18.20)
Basalt Technologies UK Ltd. (Fig. 11.1)
Beattie Passive (Fig. 3.1)
Bellway Homes (Fig. 4.36)
BOS Logistica (Fig. 6.1)
Celcon (Fig. 5.1)
ClearVuePV, West Australia (Fig. 14.3)
Curtin University, Perth, West Australia (Fig. 4.28)
Cymat Technologies Ltd. (Fig. 13.5)
De Montfort University, Leicester (Fig. 10.11)
Dyson Institute of Engineering and Technology (Fig. 4.13)
Elfin Kitchens Ltd. (Fig. 4.34)
FFLI Group, West Australia (Fig. 23.1)
Foresso Co. UK (Fig. 12.11)
FP McCann (Figs. 4.21 and 4.22)
H+H UK Ltd. (Figs. 4.23 and 5.1)
Hiltongrove (Figs. 4.25 and 4.26)
Ibstock plc. (Figs. 10.5, 10.14 and 10.15)
IMA Architects (Fig. 6.4)
Jackpad Ltd. (Figs. 7.2 and 7.3)
Jake Curtis (Figs. 12.2 and 12.4)
Kondor Pods Ltd. (Figs. 4.31, 4.32, 4.33 and 6.2)

Linda Bone and Brenda Griffiths (Fig. 12.18)

Litracon, Hungary (Fig. 11.8)

Mirreco (Figs. 4.28, 10.3, 11.5, 18.2, 18.3 and 23.1)

ModPods International Ltd. (Figs. 4.6 and 4.7)

MX3D, Thea den Heuvel and Olivier de Gruitjer (Figs. 13.3 and 13.4)

NetZeroProjects Co. (Fig. 4.29)

Nexus Modular Ltd. (Fig. 4.24)

Pan Zhenyu (Fig. 12.12)

Pilkington UK (Figs. 14.5 and 14.6)

Rise Adaptations (Fig. 6.4)

Roger Bullivant Ltd. (Fig. 7.1)

Rollforming Services in New Zealand (Fig. 4.10)

Sensitile Inc. (Fig.15.5)

TOG – The Office Group (Figs. 12.2, 12.3 and 12.4)

Vision Development South Ltd. (Figs. 4.19 and 4.20)

Water-filled Glass Technology (WFG) (Fig. 14.4)

Weston Williamson + Partners (Figs. 4.3 and 6.3)

WilkinsonEyre Architects (Fig. 4.13)

Zed Pods Ltd. (Figs. 4.8 and 4.9)

Abbreviations

3DCP	Three-Dimensional Construction Printing		CCA	Crushed Concrete Aggregate
ABLR	Automated Bricklaying Robot		CCH_2	Carbon Capture and Hydrogen
AC	Air Changes		CCS	Carbon Capture and Storage
AHSS	Advanced High Strength Steels		CCU	Carbon Capture and Use
AI	Artificial Intelligence		CCUS	Carbon Capture, Use and Storage
ALON	Aluminium Oxynitride		CFCs	Chlorofluorocarbons
AR	Augmented Reality		CG	Cellular Glass (Foamed Glass)
ASHP	Air Source Heat Pump			
ASTM	American Society for Testing and Materials		CIOB	Chartered Institute of Building
BBA	British Board of Agrément		CIS	Construction Information Systems
BCSA	British Constructional Steelwork Association		CLT	Cross-laminated Timber
BIM	Building Information Modelling		CNC	Computer Numerical Control
BIPV	Building Integrated Photovoltaic		CO	Carbon monoxide
			CO_2	Carbon dioxide
BNG	Biodiversity Net Gain		COP	Certificate of Performance
BOF	Basic Oxygen Furnace		dB	Decibel
BRE	Building Research Establishment		DfMA	Design for Manufacture and Assembly
BREEAM	Building Research Establishment Environmental Assessment Method		DLUHC	Department for Levelling Up, Housing and Communities
			DNA	Deoxyribonucleic Acid
BS EN	British Version of the European Standards		DRI	Direct Reduced Iron
			EAF	Electric Arc Furnace
BSI	British Standards Institution		ECC	Engineered Cementitious Composites
CAST	Carbon Asset Storage Technology			

EPC	Energy Performance Certificates		LSF	Light Steel Framing
EPD	Environmental Product Declaration		LVL	Laminated Veneer Lumber
			M&E	Mechanical and Electrical Services
EV	Electric Vehicle			
EVA	Ethyl Vinyl Acetate		MARSS	Materials from Alternative, Recycled and Secondary Sources
FEES	Fabric Energy Efficiency Standards			
FHS	Future Homes Standard		MBM	Meat and Bone Meal
FSC	Forest Stewardship Council		MDF	Medium Density Fibreboard
GCCMs	Geosynthetic Cementitious Composite Mats		MHCLG	Ministry of Housing, Communities and Local Government
GGBS	Ground Granulated Blast-furnace Slag		MIT	Massachusetts Institute of Technology
GluBam	Glue Laminated Bamboo		MMC	Modern Methods of Construction
GO	Graphene Oxide			
GPS	Graphite Polystyrene		MOE	Molten Oxide Electrolysis
GPS	Global Positioning System		MPa	Megapascal
GRC	Glass-fibre Reinforced Cement		MRSA	Methicillin-Resistant Staphylococcus Aureus
GRP	Glass-fibre Reinforced Plastic		MVHR	Mechanical Ventilation with Heat Recovery
HCFC	Hydrochlorofluorocarbons		NCS	Natural Color System
HEVAC	Heating, Ventilation and Air Conditioning		NHBC	National House Building Council
HRAC	Hemp and Recycled Aggregate Concrete		NO_x	Nitrogen Oxides
			OPC	Ordinary Portland Cement
HRWRA	High-Range Water Reducing Agent		OSB	Oriented Strand Board
			PCI	Pulverised Coal Injection
HS2	High Speed 2		PDLC	Polymer Dispersed Liquid Crystal
HSS	High Strength Steels			
ICB	Insulating Cork Board		PEDOT	Poly(3,4 Ethylenedioxythiophene)
ICE	Institution of Civil Engineers			
			PEFC	Programme for the Endorsement of Forest Certification scheme
ICF	Insulated Concrete Form			
IGU	Insulating Glass Unit			
ISO	International Organization for Standardization		PET	Polyethylene Terephthalate
			PIR	Passive Infrared
KGP	Potassium Geopolymeric Composite		PIR	Polyisocyanurate foam
			PMV	Pre-Manufactured Value
LED	Light-Emitting Diode		Pr BS	Draft British Standard

PU	Polyurethane foam	SCMs	Secondary Cementitious Materials
PV	Photo Voltaic	SCS	Sustainable Construction Steels
PVA	Polyvinyl Acetate		
PVB	Polyvinyl Butyral	SEB	Structural Engineered Bamboo
PVC	Polyvinyl Chloride		
PVCU	Polyvinyl Chloride Unplasticised	SIPs	Structural Insulated Panels
QR	Quick Response (code)	SPD	Suspended Particle Device
RAL	Color system – Reichs Ausschuß für Leiferbedingungen	STA	Structural Timber Association
		SuDS	Sustainable Drainage Systems
RCP	Recovered Cement Paste		
RHA	Rice Husk Ash	TDUK	Timber Development UK
RIBA	Royal Institute of British Architects	TFA	Trifluoroacetic Acid
		TRADA	Timber Research and Development Association
RICS	Royal Institution of Chartered Surveyors	UCL	University College London
RISCA	Risk, Insight, Strategy and Control Authority	UHPC	Ultra-high Performance Concrete
RMIT	Royal Melbourne Institute of Technology	UV	Ultra-violet Light
		VCL	Vapour Control Layer
RPTM	Recycled Polymer Tyre Microfibres	VIP	Vacuum Insulation Panel
		VOCs	Volatile Organic Compounds
RSTM	Recycled Steel Tyre Microfibres		
		VR	Virtual Reality
RSUF	Recycled Steel Undulating Fibres	WER	Window Energy Rating
		WFG	Water-filled Glass
SAF	Stabilised Aluminium Foam	WiFi	Wireless Fidelity
SAP	Standard Assessment Procedure	WRA	Water Reducing Agent
		WRA	Wood Recyclers' Association
SCEBs	Stabilised Compressed Earth Blocks	WWHR	Waste Water Heat Recovery
SCI	Steel Construction Institute		

CHAPTER 1

Context

Context

The UK government has set a target of net zero carbon for the whole country by 2050. To achieve this target the government has set in law the requirement to reduce total emissions by 78% by 2035 compared to the 1990 levels. To achieve this aim, the Future Homes Standard (FHS) will come into force in 2025 ensuring that all new housing is carbon neutral with low-carbon heating systems and high levels of energy efficiency. Offices and shops will have to cut emissions by 27%. Existing homes will also be subject to higher standards when being extended or upgraded. Home heating currently contributes to about 17% of the UK's total CO_2 emissions. Building and construction accounts for approximately 39% of global emissions of which operational emissions in use are 28% and 11% is from materials and construction.[1]

The new UK Building Regulations Part L, 2021 edition (England) came into force in June 2022 set standards to reduce housing CO_2 emissions by 31%. There are strict requirements for fabric U-values and ultimately no more new housing gas main connections by 2025. To achieve these rigorous targets, traditional construction may require walls of at least 300 mm thickness, involving the use of more embodied carbon materials. However, modern methods of construction (MMC), such as the manufacture of volumetric units can, under factory conditions, can achieve the required standards with less embodied carbon materials.

The new Building Regulations uplifted Part L – Conservation of Fuel and Power and Part F – Ventilation and also introduced the new Part O – Overheating. The changes act as the precursor to the anticipated 2025 Future Homes Standard (FHS) which is

DOI: 10.1201/9781003360469-1

expected to require that all new homes built from 2025 will produce 75–80% less carbon emissions than homes built to the previous regulations. The target for operational carbon reduction in the FHS[2] is backed up by Energy Performance Certificates (EPCs)[3] which may be tightened to require the use of Smart Meters to measure in-use building performance.

The Approved Document for Part L of the new regulations has two sections:

Volume 1: Dwellings

Volume 2: Buildings other than dwellings

The revised Part L regulations require a reduction in carbon emissions for new-build dwellings of 30% and for non-dwellings 27% compared to the previous 2013 edition. It is anticipated that the proposed 2025 Future Homes Standard will reduce the requirement further.

The four new Part L target metrics are:

Primary Energy Rate ($kWh_{PE}/m^2/y$) determined by the building fabric and fuel used.

Emissions Rate ($kgCO_2e/m^2/y$) determined by the building fabric and fuel used.

Fabric Energy Efficiency Rate ($kWh/m^2/y$) determined by the building fabric. (Applies to dwellings only)

Minimum Fabric and Building Services Standards.

The Primary Energy Rate includes not only the energy demand of the building, but also the energy used to supply the fuel to the building, including generation and transportation. The energy requirements for the building typically include heating, lighting and hot water.

The CO_2 Emissions Rate is used as a secondary metric supporting the Primary Energy Rate to ensure the requisite reductions in carbon emissions.

Fabric Energy Efficiency Standards (FEES) are focussed on fabric elements which directly affect the heating energy requirements of the dwelling. These include walls, roofs, floors, windows, doors, thermal bridging and air permeability. U-values of the building materials are a key factor but thermal bridging and air permeability are also significant.

The Building Regulations specify higher levels of insulation and airtightness with heating systems operating at lower temperatures appropriate to air source heat pumps. Wet space heating systems will be limited to a maximum flow temperature of 55°C. Hot water storage will be required and combi boilers will not be permitted. The replacement of gas heating by electric heat pumps does have financial implications as currently electricity is approximately 30p/KWh and gas 10p/KWh. Heat pumps have a Coefficient of Performance (COP) of 3, producing heating at 10p/KWh, and gas heating at 90% efficiency costs 11p/KWh. However, the relative costs will change significantly over time.

The changes in regulations mean that in housing built with traditional masonry cavity wall construction, the norm will be a cavity of 125 or 150 mm. Table 1.1 gives examples of typical wall formations with 150 mm cavities which achieve the required U-value of 0.18 W/m^2K.

Table 1.1 Typical housing cavity wall constructions providing a U-value of 0.18 W/m^{2}K

Full Cavity Fill

102.5 mm brickwork

150 mm cavity filled with mineral wool (λ=0.032 W/mK)

100 mm aircrete blockwork (λ=0.15–0.18 W/mK)

12.5 mm plasterboard on dabs

Partial Cavity Fill

102.5 mm brickwork

150 mm cavity partially filled with 100 mm polyisocyanurate (PIR) insulation (λ=0.022 W/mK)

100 mm medium density blockwork (λ=0.49 W/mK)

12.5 mm plasterboard on dabs

The current U-values (W/m^{2}K) for buildings other than dwellings to Building Regulations 2010 Part L Volume 2 incorporating 2023 amendments – for use in England are:

Thermal Element	Limiting U-value (W/m^{2}K)
Walls	0.26
Roofs (flat)	0.18
Roofs (pitched)	0.16
Floors	0.18
Rooflights	2.2
Pedestrian doors	1.6
Vehicle doors	1.30
High usage entrance doors	3.0
Roof ventilators (including smoke vents)	3.0
Air permeability	8.0 m^3/h.m^2 @ 50 Pa

The current U-values (W/m^{2}K) to Building Regulations 2010 incorporating 2023 amendments for use in England – Part L Volume 1: Dwellings are[4]:

Thermal Element	Limiting U-value	Suggested U-value	Extensions Limiting U-value
Walls	0.26	0.18	0.18
Roofs	0.16	0.11	0.15
Floors	0.18	0.13	0.18
Windows	1.60	1.20	1.40 band B
Rooflights	2.2	1.2 (vertical)	2.2
		1.7 (horizontal)	
Party walls	0.20	0.0	
Doors	1.6	1.0 (less than 60% glass)	
Air permeability	8.0 m^3/h.m^2 @ 50 Pa	5.0 m^3/h.m^2 @ 50 Pa	

The Building Regulations (England) do not apply to Scotland, Wales and Northern Ireland which have their own specific regulations, which are slightly different from those applicable to England.

The limiting U-values for fabric performance in new dwellings in Wales to Building Regulations 2010 – Approved Document Part L Volume 1 – 2022 edition for use in Wales are[5]:

Thermal Element	Maximum U-value (W/m²K)
Roofs	0.13
Walls – Dwelling houses	0.18
Walls – Flats	0.21
Floors	0.15
Windows, roof windows, doors	1.4
Rooflights	2.2
Party walls	0.20
Air permeability	8.0 m³/h.m² @ 50 Pa or 1.57 m³/h.m² @ 50 Pa

The limiting U-values for fabric performance in new buildings other than dwellings in Wales to Building Regulations 2010 – Approved Document Part L Volume 2 – 2022 edition for use in Wales are:

Thermal Element	Maximum U-value (W/m²K)
Wall	0.26
Roof	0.20
Floor	0.22
Windows	1.6
Roof windows	1.8
Rooflights	2.2
Pedestrian doors	1.8
Vehicle doors	1.3
High usage entrance doors	3.0
Roof ventilators (including smoke vents)	3.0
Air permeability	8.0 m³/h.m² @ 50 Pa

The limiting U-values for building elements of building fabric in new dwellings in Northern Ireland to the Building Regulations (Northern Ireland) 2012 – Technical Booklet F1 are[6]:

Thermal Element	Area weighted average U-value (W/m²K)
Wall	0.18
Floor	0.18
Roof	0.16
Windows, pedestrian doors, rooflights, curtain walling	1.4
Party wall	0.0
Air permeability	10.0 m³/h.m² @ 50 Pa

The limiting U-values for building elements of the insulated envelope in new dwellings in Scotland to the Building Regulations (Scotland) 2004 – Technical Handbook Domestic are[7]:

Thermal Element	Maximum U-value (W/m²K)
Wall	0.22
Floor	0.18
Windows, doors and rooflights	1.6
Cavity separating walls	0.20
Recommended air permeability	10.0 m³/h.m² @ 50 Pa

The anticipated 2025 Future Homes Standard regulation is expected to require all new homes to be triple glazed, with minimum standards for walls, floors and roofs. In addition the low temperature/low carbon heating would require a heat pump and waste heat recovery systems. The move to the decarbonised electricity grid would ensure that no further modifications would be necessary as fossil fuels would not be used for heating.

In response to consultation, the following U-values for the FHS have been proposed but they are subject to ratification prior to implementation in 2025:

Thermal Element	Maximum Standard U-value (W/m²K)
External Wall	0.15
Floor	0.11
Roof	0.11
Windows	0.80
Doors	1.0
Recommended air permeability	5.0 m³/h.m² @ 50 Pa

Local Authorities will be permitted to set higher energy efficiency standards for new homes in their area once the Future Homes and Buildings Standard is published.

The ecological impact of traditional construction materials is illustrated by the data on embodied carbon in Table 1.2. Many of the newer innovative materials will have significantly less environmental impact when used in construction and some will even have a negative embodied carbon impact when their carbon sequestering effect is taken into account.

The BREEAM UK New Construction scheme[8] is available to assess at the design and construction stages the environmental life-cycle impacts of new non-domestic

Table 1.2 Embodied carbon in main construction materials

Material	Embodied Carbon KgCO₂/Kg
Aluminium (European average)	6.67
Brick (clay)	0.21
Cement (OPC – CEM 1)	0.91
Cement (general average UK)	0.83
Concrete (GEN1 – 8/10 MPa)	0.90
Glass (general)	1.44
Glass (double glazing)	1.63
Steel (engineering steel)	1.27
Timber (average)	
(excludes carbon stored)	0.49
(with stored carbon)	−1.03

Note: Data from Inventory of Carbon and Energy v. 3.0, 10 November 2019 – Hammond, G. and Jones, C.

buildings within the UK. The wide range of building types covered includes office, industrial, retail, education, healthcare, residential institutions and assembly.

References

1. *Bringing embodied carbon upfront – Coordinated action for the building and construction sector to tackle embodied carbon*, 2019, World Green Building Council, London.
2. Future Homes Standard (England), UK Government, Department for Levelling Up, Housing and Communities, Expected publication date 2025.
3. *Guide to Environmental Performance Certificates (EPCs)*, Gives the energy efficiency rating of a building from A (very efficient) to G (inefficient), Energy Saving Trust, London.
4. Building Regulations England:
Approved Document B, Fire safety, Volume 1: Dwellings, 2019 edition incorporating 2020 and 2022 amendments.
Approved Document B, Fire safety, Volume 2: Buildings other than dwellings, 2019 edition incorporating 2020 and 2022 amendments.
Approved Document F, Ventilation, 2010, updated 2022.
Approved Document L, Conservation of fuel and power, Volume 1: Dwellings, 2021 edition incorporating 2023 amendments.
Approved Document L, Conservation of fuel and power, Volume 2: Buildings other than dwellings, 2021 edition incorporating 2023 amendments.
Approved Document O, Overheating, 2021, updated 2022.
5. Building Regulations Wales:
Approved Document B, Fire safety, Volume 1: Dwellinghouses, 2006 edition incorporating 2016 and 2020 amendments.
Approved Document B, Fire safety,) Volume 2: Buildings other than dwellinghouses, 2006 edition incorporating 2010, 2013, 2016 and 2020 amendments.
Approved Document, Part F, Ventilation, 2022.
Approved Document L, Conservation of fuel and power, Volume L1A: New dwellings, 2014 edition incorporating 2016 amendments.
Approved Document L, Conservation of fuel and power, Volume L1B: Existing dwellings, 2014 edition incorporating 2016 amendments.
Approved Document L, Conservation of fuel and power, Volume L2A: New buildings other than dwellings, 2014 edition incorporating 2016 amendments.
Approved Document L, Conservation of fuel and power, Volume L2B: Existing buildings other than dwellings, 2014 edition incorporating 2016 amendments.
Building Regulations Guidance: Part O, Overheating, 2022.
6. Building Regulations Northern Ireland:
Building Regulations (Northern Ireland) 2012, Part E, Fire Safety.
Building Regulations (Northern Ireland) 2012, Part F, Conservation of fuel and power.
Building Regulations (Northern Ireland) 2012, Part K, Ventilation.

7. Building Regulations Scotland: Building Standards Technical Handbook 2023: Domestic.
Building Standards Technical Handbook 2023: Non-domestic.

8. Building Research Establishment, BREEAM UK New Construction, Version 6, Reference SD5079, 24/08/2022.

CHAPTER 2

Introduction to Modern Methods of Construction

CONTENTS

Introduction to MMC

As the country moves towards zero carbon by 2050, innovations in construction will play an increasingly important part of the national plan. Currently, building construction and operational emissions contribute approximately 38% of total carbon output. To achieve the ultimate net zero target, a reduction of 50% will be required by 2030.

The text covers the developing area of Modern Methods of Construction (MMC), which is currently being promoted by the UK government[1] and is being picked up by a significant number of major players in building construction, particularly within the housing market. It is claimed that modular construction systems could cut carbon emissions by up to 45% compared to traditional building techniques. The UK government agency Homes England[2] has given significant financial support to Britain's modular housing sector.

However, the uptake of modular construction across the UK is still modest, with only 8% of new housing built by off-site modular techniques in 2021. Some companies focussing on MMC for the housing market have gone into administration with significant financial losses, leading to other firms being wary of investing in modular factories. One reason for the company failures appears to be over provision of manufacturing capacity due to the slower-than-anticipated uptake in the market not only for residential but also in the hotel and education sectors. Modular factories need a constant throughput of work to retain operational competitiveness. Another factor

DOI: 10.1201/9781003360469-2

is the general caution in the construction industry about insurance issues especially after the Grenfell Tower[3] disaster although that particular building was constructed using traditional systems. One manufacturer of modular housing reported that design defects in their homes had led to a loss of customer confidence and the subsequent collapse of the company. The issue of consumer trust was raised by the CIOB and BRE in the UK House of Lords Built Environment Committee report 'Meeting Housing Demand'.[4] A further inhibiting factor is possibly the requirement of some modular firms to require significant upfront payments from clients to cover initial costs.

On the positive side, it is argued that the construction of modular housing is speedier, offers better factory, rather than building site, working conditions and requires significantly less transport movements. On site work is reduced to about one-fifth of what is required for traditionally constructed housing. Student accommodation and built-to-rent projects are particularly suited to modular construction due to their repetitive nature. The typical College Road modular development by Vision Modular Systems® and Tide Construction® at Croydon[5,6] (Figure 2.1) consists of two towers of 50 and 35 storeys offering 817 co-living and 120 affordable homes. The 50-storey tower at 150 metres is currently the world's tallest residential modular building.

It is understood that the British Standards Institution (BSI) is working with the UK government's Department for Levelling Up, Housing and Communities (DLUHC) on the production of a British Standard for MMC[7] which will encompass recommended technical standards for the

Figure 2.1 College Road, Croydon. Modular housing development of twin 50- and 35-metre towers. Photograph: Arthur Lyons

production of homes manufactured by the full range of off-site systems.

References

1. *Modern Methods of Construction – Guidance Notes*, Government Commercial Function, 2022, Crown Copyright.
2. Homes England: Non-departmental public body set up in 2018 that funds new affordable housing in England.
3. Grenfell Tower: 24 Storey tower block fire in London which led to the deaths of 72 residents in 2017.

4. House of Lords Built Environment Committee, 'Meeting Housing Demand' 1st report of session 2021–2022, Published by Authority of the House of Lords on 10 January 2022.

5. Vision Modular Systems UK Ltd., (https://wwwvisionmodular.com), Bedford.

6. Tide Construction Ltd., (https://tideconstruction.co.uk), London.

7. *Boost for modern homebuilding as government launches work with industry to set UK-wide standard.* British Standards Institution, 2023, BSI, London.

CHAPTER 3

Modern Methods of Construction – Categories and Benefits

CONTENTS

Introduction

The chapter describes the seven categories of Modern Methods of Construction (MMC) as defined by the UK Government's Ministry of Housing, Communities and Local Government framework[1]. The framework was generated in 2019 by a joint working group incorporating Buildoffsite, Homes England, NHBC[2] and the RICS to regularise the terminology used by all stakeholders. The chapter describes the systems that have to date proved the most popular within the building industry, and also cites the benefits that are achieved by modular as opposed to traditional construction.

Categories of Modern Methods of Construction

Modern Methods of Construction are seen by government and many building developers as the key to increasing productivity and delivery of construction particularly in the housing sector. One manufacturer is intending to set up regional manufacturing hubs for localised production of housing, schools and hospitals. However, the quest for standardisation cannot go too far, as although, for example, bathrooms may be similar in schools and hospitals, the requirements for housing may be much more diverse.

DOI: 10.1201/9781003360469-3

There are several types of MMC, which in principle all involve the off-site production of components, offering faster build times, reduced costs and a reduction in building materials waste. Also factory-constructed units can afford tighter quality control on tolerances and finishes compared to some on-site techniques. Factory-based robots can accurately cut, drill, nail, weld, screw, glue and spray paint. MMC is particularly favoured for the housing market as standardised units can be repeated in the production process.

The term MMC covers a wide range of systems from the modular construction of 3-D units, the production of pods, such as factory-assembled kitchens and bathrooms, the off-site manufacture panelised systems and sub-assemblies such as pre-fabricated roofs down to small units such as pre-assembled cabling systems.

The key categories of off-site or near-site MMC as defined by the UK Government's Ministry of Housing, Communities and Local Government framework are:

Category 1 3D Primary Structural Systems – volumetric modules (Figure 3.1).

Category 2 2D Primary Structural Systems – panelised and framed systems.

Category 3 Pre-manufactured Components – off-site manufactured structural units.

Category 4 Additive manufacturing – on- or off-site manufacture by digital printing techniques.

Category 5 Pre-manufacturing of non-structural assemblies and sub-assemblies – volumetric units (pods).

Figure 3.1 Volumetric modular homes built to Passivhaus[3] standards using Modern Methods of Construction at the Beattie Passive[4] off-site factory in Norfolk. Photograph: Courtesy of Beattie Passive

The framework was designed to regularise terminology and to increase the proportion of pre-manufactured value (PMV) within the construction industry. In addition to the five on- or near-site categories, two categories related to on-site process improvements are included within the umbrella of MMC:

Category 6 Traditional building product enhancement (e.g. the use of large format blockwork).

Category 7 On-site labour reduction and productivity improvements (e.g. the use of insulated formwork, systemised in-situ concrete systems such as tunnel form, robotic bending of steel rebar, the use of BIM to enhance workflow, the use of GPS as a site planning tool).

A white paper[5] in November 2020 by Architects Data File reported the following methods of off-site construction preferred by the construction industry. Panelised timber systems were the most popular followed by steel frame then structural insulated panels (SIPS) and cross-laminated timber (CLT). The survey also showed that architects generally felt that housing was the most appropriate sector for offsite construction, closely followed by education and student housing. Some architectural practices were using BIM (Building Information Modelling) to optimise their off-site designs, but concern was expressed over the challenge to achieve high-quality design and the avoidance of homogeneity within projects. As MMC are extended, it is anticipated that architectural practice design work will move progressively towards DfMA (Design for Manufacture and Assembly) and further away from the more traditional role.

Benefits of Modular Construction

Modular construction affords a wide range of advantages compared to traditional building techniques[6]. Factory operations are significantly faster than working on site which is heavily dependent on weather conditions and at certain times requires the erection of scaffolding for access or the use of specialist equipment. Repeatability ensures that the manufacture of components or built units is faster, more reliable and the necessary quality control can be more rigorous under factory conditions where visual inspections and snagging are easier and more quickly executed. Critically, overall the manufacturing processes are more energy efficient. Typically 67% less energy is consumed to produce a modular building when compared to traditional methods. On site the fabricated units can be fixed in much less time than is required for traditional building techniques such as bricklaying and placing concrete.

Modular construction requires fewer labourers on site, which significantly reduces building costs and addresses the issue of shortages in the experienced workforce. It is anticipated that over the next fifteen years, the construction industry will lose half a million workers due to retirement and the lack of new skilled labour entering the profession. With modular construction, generally less specialist equipment is required on site, except for the necessary lifting gear required for placement of the modular units or components.

The construction industry, as a whole, produces 60% of all waste in the UK, much of which ends up in landfill sites. Modular construction under factory conditions using BIM (Building Information Modelling) assists building project managers with ordering exactly the right quantities to avoid waste and thereby cut costs. Generally, modular buildings are easier to deconstruct as a reverse of the building process. This enables more materials to be reused or recycled.

Another advantage of off-site construction is the significant reduction in road transport deliveries around the building site. This can be a reduction of up to 90% fewer vehicle movements. Also as the construction work on site is much quicker than traditional processes, disturbances to nearby residents are reduced. The reduction in traffic movements also reduces carbon emissions and limits dust and pollution within the vicinity.

It is estimated[7] that the modular towers of 44 and 38 storeys built designed by HTA Design and developed by VMS[8] (Vision Modular Systems®) and Tide Construction®[9] at George Street, Croydon (Figure 3.2) had over 40% less embodied carbon than traditional build. Two tower blocks were constructed over a two year period with modules craned up to surround the two central concrete construction cores. The blocks were constructed as flats to rent. Over 1500 modules were built off site in Bedford and now provide 546 new homes together with social areas including gyms, gardens, residents' lounges, café and art gallery. The main façade incorporates large green format terracotta cladding, glazed balustrades and featured metalwork.

Currently around 8% of UK's total construction output is modular building and it is anticipated that by 2032 around 20% of all new homes will be of modular construction.

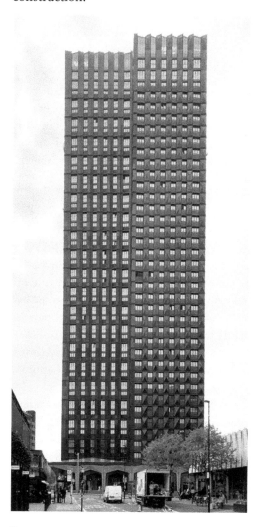

Figure 3.2 Twin modular towers of 38 and 44 storeys, 'Ten Degrees', George Street, Croydon. Designed by HTA Design and developed by Tide Construction with Greystar Properties and Vision Modular Systems. Photograph: Arthur Lyons

References

1. *Modern Methods of Construction – Introducing the MMC Definition Framework*, Website: MMC-I-Padbase_GOVUK-FINAL_SECURE.pdf (https://cast-consultancy.com).
2. *Modern Methods of Construction – Who is doing what?*, NHBC Foundation Milton Keynes, 2018, ISBN 978-1-9995997-1-3.
3. *What is Passivhaus? The gold standard in energy efficiency*, 25 July 2022, Energy Saving Trust, London.
4. Beattie Passive: Passivhaus Modular Homes, (https://www.beattiepassive.com), Norwich.
5. *Exploring Current Thinking in Offsite Construction*, Architects Data File, 5 November 2020, (www.architectsdatafile.co.uk), netMAGmedia Ltd., Tonbridge.
6. *Offsite modular construction. Modern methods of construction are shaping the way we build efficiently and sustainably.* (https://bregroup.com/expertise/innovation/modular-construction/), BRE, Watford.
7. *Modular construction emits 45% less carbon than traditional methods, report finds.* Lowe, T., 6 June 2022, Building, London.
8. Vision Modular Systems UK Ltd., (https://wwwvisionmodular.com), Bedford.
9. Tide Construction Ltd., (https://tideconstruction.co.uk), London.

CHAPTER 4

Off-Site Modern Methods of Construction

CONTENTS

DOI: 10.1201/9781003360469-4

Introduction

The five off-site pre-manufacturing categories of Modern Methods of Construction (MMC) ranging from 3D primary structural systems down to the production of non-structural assemblies and pods, as defined by the MMC Framework,[1] are explained. The first categories have the highest levels of pre-manufactured value[2] (PMV).

Category 1 3D Primary Structural Systems (Volumetric Modules)

Volumetric modules are pre-engineered units that have usually been fully fitted out under factory conditions with all fixtures and fittings and are ready to be installed on site as building block units, although some units are manufactured just as the basic structure for subsequent fitting out on site. In some cases the units are complete with external cladding and roofing systems. The majority of units are manufactured from timber or steel. Modules are transported to site and located on preformed foundations or stacked to form multi-storey construction. The unit size is limited by local transportation constraints. This form of MMC has been greatly favoured recently as on-site work is restricted to the minimum compared to other less sophisticated MMC systems. This type of construction can reduce build times by between 50% and 60% compared to traditional processes. Quality of construction can be more easily assured,

reducing financial risk and the potential of costly legal disputes. The advantages of economy of scale can be capitalised upon more readily in controlled off-site conditions, and this factor applies both for housing and for high-rise accommodation such as student residences. The 'Chapter' Lewisham development (Figures 4.1, 4.2 and 4.3) consisting of two twelve-storey blocks, built with 636 modules, provides 611 student bedrooms. On-site construction work was completed within ten months. Volumetric units for apartment buildings may include not only the repetitive accommodation units but also larger communal spaces. Additionally small 'off-grid' units are frequently totally factory-manufactured for immediate location on site.

Steel Frame Volumetric Housing

The rectangular volumetric modules for ilke Homes®[4] (Figures 4.4 and 4.5) are manufactured from galvanised steel frames with floors insulated with mineral wool and rigid polyisocyanurate (PIR) foam. External steel frame walls are insulated with mineral wool, and the roofs constructed from timber trusses also insulated with mineral wool. Externally the airtight modules, featuring low thermal bridging, can be finished in brickwork giving an overall high performance of building fabric. Together with LED lighting, air source heat pump (ASHP), integrated solar photovoltaic (PV) panels and battery storage the homes are virtually net zero in energy consumption.

Figure 4.1 Twin 12-storey blocks of high-rise student accommodation in Lewisham, London built by modular construction. 'Chapter' was designed by Weston Williamson + Partners and built by Tide Construction.[3] Photograph: Arthur Lyons

Figure 4.2 The main entrance to 'Chapter' student accommodation in Lewisham, London. Photograph: Arthur Lyons

Figure 4.3 The tight site for 'Chapter' student accommodation in Lewisham, London – located adjacent to the railway line. Photograph: Courtesy of Weston Williamson + Partners

Figure 4.4 Modular housing at 'The Sidings', Beeston, Nottinghamshire. Houses built by ilke Homes in their factory at Knaresborough, North Yorkshire. Photograph: Susan Lyons

Figure 4.5 'The Sidings' Beeston, Nottinghamshire development comprising 42 affordable off-site constructed homes adjacent to the local train station. Photograph: Arthur Lyons

Figure 4.6 Three storey steel frame modular housing clad in brickwork. Photograph: Courtesy of ModPods International Ltd.

ModPods International® houses[5] (Figures 4.6 and 4.7) are manufactured with a steel frame, fully insulated to current building regulations and incorporate sustainable energy technologies including solar photovoltaic systems and water harvesting. The ModPod Zero® houses incorporate triple glazing, infrared ceiling

Figure 4.7 Two storey steel-frame modular housing with metal cladding. Photograph: Courtesy of ModPods International Ltd.

Figure 4.8 Steel frame volumetric housing on a steel podium built by Zed Pods Ltd. for the London Borough of Bromley. Photograph: Arthur Lyons

heating, waste water heat recovery (WWHR), mechanical ventilation with heat recovery (MVHR), smart electrical points and EV car charging facilities.

The Zed Pods®[6] homes in Bromley, Kent (Figures 4.8 and 4.9) are steel-framed volumetric units built on a steel podium above the residential car parking spaces

Figure 4.9 Zed Pods Ltd. housing at Bromley illustrating accessibility from residents' parking. Photograph: Susan Lyons

below, within a wider zone offering public car parking spaces. The mixture of one- and two-bed apartments incorporate triple glazing, MVHR, EV car charging points, secure bicycle storage and offer high levels of natural daylighting. Six of the units are wheelchair accessible with a dedicated lift arrangement. The form of construction, together with on-site renewable energy generation with photovoltaic panels and solar-assisted heat pumps, gives the development an overall SAP A-rating.

The off-site construction sequence used by Rollforming Services[7] (Figure 4.10) is typical for light steel-framed systems commencing with manufacture of the floor units with their necessary boarding and servicing, followed by the attachment of the steel frame ready-lined and painted wall assemblies. The ceiling frames are then added. The subsequent fit–out includes all necessary plumbing and wiring including the installation of bathrooms and other fittings as appropriate. A full fit-out may include carpets, furniture, electrics for ancillary equipment including TV and air conditioning units as specified. When the services systems are complete and tested, insulation is inserted into the wall and ceiling framing and the whole module is enveloped in a protective cover for safe transportation to site. On site the

Figure 4.10 Steel bathroom pod framing. Photograph: Courtesy of Rollforming Services in New Zealand

units are craned into position and securely joined together. Services can then be connected, followed by the addition of the roofing system and external cladding.

Steel as a non-combustible material does not contribute to the fire load of a building, and can be protected internally by the use of non-combustible boards, such as fibre cement or plasterboard for the linings. Fire resistance periods of up to 120 minutes are achievable. Furthermore, steel can be fully recycled when the building is demolished. Also, as a lightweight construction system, the concrete required for building foundations is significantly less than with heavier traditional construction systems such as masonry thus reducing the overall embodied CO_2.

Timber Frame Volumetric Housing

One typical production system is based on modules constructed in structural insulated panels (SIPs) which are fully finished including brick cladding, glazing, kitchen and bathroom units and all wiring and plumbing before transportation to site. SIPs are usually made from two layers of OSB (oriented strand board) encasing insulation – either injected self-bonding polyurethane foam or adhesively-bonded expanded polystyrene. On-site completion usually requires only services connections and some external features such as rainwater pipes, the necessary module joints and extras such as an additional porch. Standard alternative structural materials include cross-laminated timber (CLT) and glulam. For housing, manufacturers expect to offer many variations, particularly on external features, to avoid repetitiveness in

the final schemes and on internal alternatives to be customised by the purchaser. Houses are typically constructed from two or three volumetric units, but high-rise can also be constructed by the stacking of modules. The finishing touches to the Urban Splash[®8] town houses at Inholm, Northstowe, (Figures 4.11 and 4.12) including external brickwork cladding, take about eight to ten weeks to complete after delivery and placing of the modules. Volumetric units for apartment buildings can include both the individual apartments and the communal spaces. Road transport is usually limited to a maximum of one or two units per delivery. Timber volumetric is used extensively in Scandinavian countries where harsher weather conditions require buildings to be constructed quickly.

The elegant student housing for the campus of the Dyson Institute of Engineering and Technology, designed by WilkinsonEyre Architects (Figure 4.13) was constructed entirely from CLT (cross-laminated timber) volumetric modules. The $32m^2$ modules were fabricated in Scotland and fully fitted out with bathroom units, electrics and fixed furniture. The units were then transported to Dyson's Wiltshire campus where the aluminium rainscreen cladding was added. The volumetric units were craned into position in clusters of up to six, incorporating a three-meter cantilever to enhance the visual effect. The use of concrete for the foundations was kept to a minimum and the site was enhanced by the planting of wild flowers and the incorporation of a bund necessary to give access to the upper storeys. Sedum-covered roofs attenuate the rainwater run-off into a small brook. The units are highly energy efficient

Figure 4.11 Modular housing at 'The Penninsula' Inholm, Northstowe, Cambridgeshire. Houses constructed by Urban Splash/Homes England. Photograph: Arthur Lyons

Figure 4.12 Northstowe modular housing illustrating the stacked units prior to the addition of external cladding. Photograph: Arthur Lyons

Figure 4.13 Cross-laminated timber student accommodation at the Dyson Institute of Engineering and Technology, Malmesbury, designed by WilkinsonEyre Architects. Photograph: Courtesy of WilkinsonEyre Architects and the Dyson Institute of Engineering and Technology

capitalising on the thermal massing of CLT and natural ventilation.

Concrete Volumetric Units

Concrete volumetric units most commonly include primary structural systems such as stair or lift cores. However, inHAUS®[9] in Spain manufactures concrete volumetric housing units. The custom-built and standard villa-type houses are 90% manufactured in the Valencia factory for subsequent transportation to site. The individual units can be stacked creating interesting two-storey cantilever or bridge effects as required.

Commercial Buildings

Lewisham Exchange, (Figures 4.14 and 4.15) built by Tide Construction®, is currently the tallest 3D volumetric structural modular student accommodation in Europe. The two blocks, of 20 and 35 storeys, reaching over 100 m in height, provide 750 student apartments and around 70 affordable homes. The 1251 steel modular units, complete with fitted windows, were hoisted and fixed to the buildings' central lift cores, and were finished on site with Mechslip®[10] brick slip cladding. The A1 fire-rated system incorporates

Figure 4.14 Twin tower blocks – 'Lewisham Exchange'. The units were manufactured off site by Vision Modular[12] and built on site by Tide Construction. Photograph: Susan Lyons

28 mm Ibstock®[11] brick slips mechanically secured and pre-spaced with a 10 mm joint for pointing, which gives the towers a natural brick aesthetic. The concrete commercial properties at the base of the building achieved a BREEAM 'Excellent' rating.

Building under factory-controlled conditions, rather than on site, can more easily ensure that construction reaches the required environmental standards. For example, the Foleshill Health Centre (Figures 4.16 and 4.17) built by volumetric modular construction and completed in 2021 achieved better than required performance for Passivhaus standard[13] as well as receiving a BREEAM 'Excellent' rating. The building's 14-module superstructure used Portakabin's®[14] largest module size and achieved an air tightness of 0.525AC/h@50 Pa compared to the Passivhaus limit of 0.6AC/h@50 Pa.

In the education sector, the modular extension to Gartree High School (Figure 4.18) was required to match the existing school building and provide an additional four classrooms. The unit was completed to a high standard with triple glazing, air conditioning and PIR-controlled lighting. The client confirmed that construction with a modular system was more easily managed than a traditional building programme.

Analysis by Swansea University[15] showed that volumetric modules produced by Seismic® have low carbon impacts when, design, materials, manufacturing and logistics were considered cumulatively. A standard Seismic® module comprises 581.3kgCO$_2$e per m^2, which is significantly below the BRE Construction 2025's target

Figure 4.15 The ground floor accommodation of 'Lewisham Exchange' provides commercial outlets. Photograph: Arthur Lyons

Figure 4.16 Foleshill Health Centre, Coventry. A Design for Manufacture and Assembly (DfMA) building by Portakabin. Photograph: Arthur Lyons

Figure 4.17 Foleshill Health Centre, Coventry, main canopy entrance. Photograph: Arthur Lyons

Figure 4.18 Gartree High School, Oadby, Leicestershire. The new modular building matches in architectural style with the earlier traditional building. Photograph: Arthur Lyons

of $1300kgCO_2e$ per m^2. Furthermore, as the modules can be reused by relocation to other sites, or refurbished for different use, this adds a further $234kgCO_2e$ per m^2 clawback.

Category 2 2D Primary Structural Systems (Panelised and Framed Systems)

Panelised construction involves the production of flat panels for assembly on site. The units such as floors, roofs, internal and external walls may be fitted out in the factory as closed panels with appropriate windows, doors and insulation prior to transportation to the site. Alternatively, windows and doors may be fitted on site. Clearly transportation of flat panels is easier than large 3D volumetric modules. Panelised systems are typically manufactured in timber frame, structural insulated panels (SIPs), cross-laminated timber (CLT), light-gauge steel or pre-cast concrete[16].

Timber Closed Panel Systems

The closed panel system of timber construction consists of a structural frame which is factory fitted with insulation and inner boards. Some systems include pre-fitted windows, servicing systems and plasterboard internal finish. At the higher end of pre-manufactured value (PMV), which is a measure of the project's off-site construction, external cladding may be factory fitted. A reflective, low-emissivity membrane may be included to enhance energy efficiency and a protective membrane is usually applied to prevent damage during transportation.

The Greencore Homes[®17] closed panel system incorporates lime-hemp and wood-fibre insulation to produce energy-efficient homes built to Passivhaus principles which lock up more carbon than is emitted during their construction. The external wall panels lock up $32kgCO_2e/m^2$ and the CLT used for upper floors and small areas of flat roofing sequester $125kgCO_2e/m^2$. Construction incorporates triple glazing, minimal thermal bridging, high levels of air-tightness, photovoltaic (PV) panels and mechanical ventilation with heat recovery (MVHR). The external walls have a U-value of 0.15 W/m^2K. Detailed analysis[18] of whole life emissions for one house on the Springfields Meadows development in Southmoor, Oxfordshire suggests that the property should have whole-life carbon emissions of $-278kgCO_2e/m^2$, compared to the RIBA (Royal Institute of British Architects) 2030 target of $+625kgCO_2e/m^2$ for domestic housing.

An Austrian company[19] (Stora Enso®) has developed a system which automatically applies a water-based coating to the CLT wall and floor units to give greater protection against moisture, sunlight, insects and fire. The material also gives a pleasantly coloured surface.

Timber Open Panel Systems

The timber open panel system (Figures 4.19 and 4.20) provides the basic structural frame. Insulation may be incorporated, but windows are fitted on site. Timber panels are typically manufactured from 140 × 38 mm timber, but if extra insulation is required, additional timber can be added as a spacer. The basic frame

Figure 4.19 Timber open panel construction. Photograph: Courtesy of Vision Development South Ltd.[20] – Timber Frame Supply and Erect

Figure 4.20 Timber open panel constructed housing awaiting the external cladding. Photograph: Courtesy of Vision Development South Ltd. – Timber Frame Supply and Erect

is braced by factory-fitted rigid boards usually of plywood or oriented strand board (OSB) which are nailed firmly in place. On site the timber open panels are located and fixed to each other to form the rigid timber frame structure. Insulation and service runs are incorporated into the panels which are then closed with a vapour control layer and plasterboard or gypsum-fibre board. The exterior faces of the panels are covered with a breather membrane which permits the escape of any moisture in the system. Typical exterior cladding materials are softwood boarding, GRC, tiles or render. Alternatively, a separate masonry leaf may be added for aesthetic reasons.

Concrete Crosswall Construction

Concrete crosswall construction[21] (Figure 4.21) incorporates precast floors and load-bearing walls and is appropriate for buildings of a cellular nature such as student accommodation, hotels, apartments and prisons. The load-bearing walls give primary vertical support and lateral stability. This is further stabilised by the lift shafts or staircase core walls. This form of construction offers good thermal mass, acoustic performance and fire resistance. The units are increasingly manufactured using higher-strength, self-compacting concrete (C35/45 grade) reducing the use of vibrators to compact the concrete and thus improving factory working conditions. Walls, usually incorporating two layers of mesh reinforcement, are typically 150–170 mm thick, but 180 mm is common for party walls for acoustic reasons. Precast solid floors are typically 200–250 mm thick. After craning into position, the walls are propped up until stabilised by the fixing of the floor above. Units are tied together with a series of hidden joints which are pressure grouted

Figure 4.21 Concrete crosswall construction for Selly Oak, Birmingham student accommodation. Photograph: Courtesy of FP McCann

as construction proceeds. Exterior walls can be constructed using sandwich panels which may incorporate brick or render finish as required. Alternative finishes include smooth and acid etched with colours ranging from terracotta and off-white to azure and charcoal. Buildings up to 22 storeys have been constructed within the UK using crosswall systems.

The Marriott Hotel in Manchester (Figure 4.22) incorporated approximately 1000 individual concrete units comprising 180 mm thick crosswalls, 200 mm floor slabs and 695 mm thick insulated brick-faced façade panels together with precast stair and lift cores. The precast units were delivered on a 'just-in-time' basis enabling the erection of an entire floor every two weeks.

Concrete Wall and Panel Systems

Pre-fabricated concrete walls for the external structural skin of a building have the advantage that they can be load-bearing up to a height of typically eight storeys and precast floor units can span without requiring additional sub-frames.

Figure 4.22 Precast off-site building solutions – the Marriott Hotel, Manchester. Photograph: Courtesy of FP McCann

Load-bearing cladding systems typically consist of an inner structural layer, insulation and a non-structural outer panel. A wide range of finishes are available including plain or pigmented concrete, rendering, texturing, acid etching and polishing.

Figure 4.23 illustrates fast wall construction using full height concrete panels.

Concrete panels may be manufactured with traditional concrete or with aircrete which is lighter to handle and fix on site. Panels may be clad with brick slips to reduce on-site work. The complete shell of a house can be completed within a week using H+H® aircrete 2325 mm storey-high panels. Aircrete panels with a width of 600 mm

Figure 4.23 Full height Celcon® vertical wall panels manufactured in aircrete. Photograph: Courtesy of H+H UK Ltd.[22]

and a thickness of 100 mm are craned into place to form the inner leaf of the external walls and any internal partitions. The panels are located onto traditional foundations and jointed with 2 mm quick-setting joints to give an airtight enclosure. Door and window openings can be cut on site. Party walls can be produced using two 100 mm panels with full-fill insulation ensuring no heat loss and good acoustic insulation. Where design variations are required, additional work can be done with standard thin-joint 100 mm large format blockwork. Following the construction of the basic panel structure, the insulation and external leaf of the cavity wall can be added together with the prefabricated floor and roof systems. The whole operation gives full enclosure to a basic house structure within five days on site. Panels have a typical thermal conductivity of λ = 0.17 W/mK.

An alternative system[23] (SpecWall®) offers precast concrete panels with tongue & groove joints for speedy erection. Standard panel sizes are 610 × 3000 mm with thickness of 75 mm and 100 mm. Elevations above the standard panel height of 3000 mm can be unsupported to a maximum of 5 m for the 75 mm boards and 6 m for the 100 mm boards. For these extended heights, the horizontal joints should be staggered. Door and window openings do not require a lintel but are headed with a horizontal panel to a maximum width of 2600 mm. Joints are bonded with polyurethane adhesive and filled with grout to ensure soundproofing. A twin wall can be formed with appropriate thermal and acoustic insulation and penetrations for services are cut on site. The bases of the panels are slotted and fixed into U-shaped channels which are in turn fixed

at 600 mm centres to the supporting substrate. U-channels are 20 mm deep for both thicknesses of panel. Panel heads are fixed with 50 × 50 mm or 75 × 75 mm steel angle sections as appropriate. Necessary movement joints are filled with mineral wool insulation and sealed with intumescent mastic for fire protection. Panel corners are secured by a dowel which penetrates into each panel by at least 100 mm. Where steel beams are exposed, cut panels can be used for fire protection. Walls can be finished with tiles or plaster skim and paint as required. The system can reduce significantly the time required on site for the erection of walls compared to traditional techniques.

Concrete Frame Systems

Laing O'Rouke has developed a new precast concrete frame system which has beam-to-beam connections which resist distortion[24]. The M-Frame® system relies on the moment resisting connections to produce structural continuity between the precast concrete components negating the requirement for intermediate support at the joints, effectively creating larger clear spans. The novel D-Frame® system[25] has a connection system which enables the precast concrete structure to be deconstructed and reused or reconfigured offering a major contribution to the circular economy.

Light Steel Frame Systems

Cold-rolled light steel framing (LSF) (Figures 4.24, 4.25 and 4.26) has the advantage that for an equivalent structure it is about half the weight of concrete which therefore

Figure 4.24 Cold rolled steel modules being assembled by the construction team after craning up to the top of the site. Photograph: Courtesy of Nexus Modular Ltd.[26]

Figure 4.25 Cold rolled steel sections erected. Photograph: Courtesy of Hiltongrove,[27] Hamza I. Kadeen

Figure 4.26 Awaiting the addition of external cladding to the steel frame structure. Photograph: Courtesy of Hiltongrove, Hamza I. Kadeen

15 mm layers of fire-resistant plasterboard or the use of calcium silicate board in conjunction with plasterboard.

Flat sections are manufactured directly from the architect's 3D model and craned into position on site, where they are fixed down and bolted together to form the rigid structure. Where appropriate, stairs and lift shafts are incorporated as each floor is constructed eliminating the need for external scaffolding to give access to upper levels. At each level, plasterboard packs and bathroom / kitchen pods can be inserted. Metal decking is then installed to be followed by poured concrete to form a floor with high fire and acoustic performance. The process is repeated floor by floor with follow-on trades able to operate when each level is complete. Finally the roof is installed, either flat with steel decking and concrete, or pitched with a lightweight steel or timber system and appropriate finish.

Lightweight steel frame systems offer the flexibility to incorporate variations such as balconies and walkways, also a variety of external finishes including non-combustible panels or masonry are generally possible. A combination of BIM technology and Design for Manufacture and Assembly (DfMA) protocols ensures minimal waste in the production process and less snagging on site.

reduces the total embodied CO_2, furthermore, the material is fully recyclable and reuseable. Structural stability is usually provided by incorporation of cross bracing, rather than reliance on sheet diaphragm action with OSB or plywood as in the case for timber framing. Fire protection for light steel framing is typically provided by non-combustible boards. Typical fire protection ranges from 60 to 90 minutes; however, when the structural steel framing requires a higher level of protection, 120 minutes can be achieved with three

Category 3 Pre-manufactured Components

Individual elements such as pre-assembled roofs, wall panels and chimney stacks can be incorporated into traditional construction or as part of a MMC solution.

Typical types of precast concrete floor units include solid, hollowcore, coffered, lattice girder slabs and double-tee units. Other standard precast concrete units include wall sections, beams, columns, stairs, balconies and small infrastructure elements. Concrete elements may be pre-stressed in the factory allowing thinner sections to be used. Units can be manu-factured to incorporate other building elements, for example, service conduits within wall panels. Pre-manufactured brick units include lintels and arches.

Light gauge steel panels for walls, floors and roofs are manufactured with features such as doors, windows, insulation, cladding, fire stopping and vents to the specifier's requirements. Timber pre-manufactured components include glulam structural members, trussed rafters and dormer units. Figure 4.27 illustrates an automated nailing machine for fast pro-duction of timber panels. The machine holds the panel square and fixings are controlled by CNC (Computerized Numerical Control).

Category 4 Additive Manufacturing

Additive manufacturing includes the pro-duction of structural or non-structural

Figure 4.27 The Modular Building Automation[28] (MBA®) machine for timber frame assembly. Photograph: Arthur Lyons

elements based on digital computer-based systems, such as 3D-printing of concrete or hempcrete as illustrated by Figure 4.28.

Minimass®[30] uses geometry optimisation of the concrete within beams to significantly reduce materials and weight, whilst increasing efficiency. This can be achieved by 3D-printing of the concrete as well as traditional precast methods. Minimass beams (Figure 4.29) incorporate

external post-tensioning steel cables and may incorporate reinforcement in the top chord if required. They are particularly suited to long-span construction such as floor beams and pitched roofs.

3D-Printed Concrete Construction

It is anticipated that the 3D-printing construction market may reach over $0.87 billion

Figure 4.28 3D-digital printer for the production of printed concrete or hempcrete building units. Photograph: Courtesy of Mirreco®[29] and Curtin University, Perth, West Australia

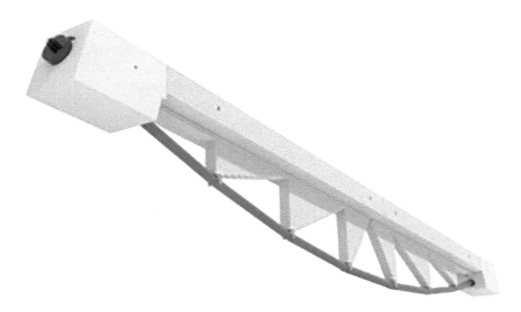

Figure 4.29 3D-printed Minimass®concrete beam which is formed using geometry optimisation to reduce materials and weight whilst increasing efficiency. Photograph: Courtesy of NetZeroProjects Co

by 2026, with growth in housing, schools and offices[31]. The system offers lower waste of materials as placement of concrete can be exactly where it is structurally required with no requirement for formwork. Furthermore, complex shapes can be produced which would be difficult to manufacture by conventional systems. Productivity is efficient and less manual labour is required. Materials will not be limited to concrete as research is already being undertaken on the use of hemp-based material.

Some limitations on the uptake of the technology are the high initial investment costs of the equipment and the need for highly skilled technical staff to operate and maintain the system. In addition, there is some reluctance to accept the undulating surface finish produced by the printing process. However, Dubai aims to have a quarter of its buildings constructed using 3D-printing by 2030, as it is claimed that labour costs, materials and waste are all reduced by around 50%.[32]

The technology of 3D-printing of concrete is developing rapidly through a combination of digital technology and robotics. The delivery of the concrete mix through a nozzle on a gantry or mobile robot is controlled directly from the digitized building model. The rheology of the concrete mix or mortar is critical to ensure flow through the nozzle and stability of the delivered material. Necessarily the pumpable mix must cure rapidly but also adhere to the previously cast layer. This is achieved using geopolymer concrete, frequently based on ggbs (ground granulated blast-furnace slag) with admixtures. Typical mixes are 70% cementitious material and 30% aggregate with a maximum aggregate size of 3 mm to permit nozzle discharge. A setting time of five to eight minutes between layers is typical, with load-bearing after one hour. Fibre reinforcement is usually incorporated into the mix, and a recent development is the use of microscopic graphene strands. Traditional reinforcement can be incorporated into the design as the nozzle which moves up to $^1/_2$m per second can be programmed to deliver the mix around and through rebars. External weather conditions need to be considered as temperature and humidity affect the stability of the delivered material. A significant advantage of the 3D-printing process is the virtual elimination of on-site waste giving potential savings of between 5% and 25%, and sophisticated 3D forms can be produced. The final strength of the material depends on the mix, but a typical construction would have 28-day compressive and tensile strengths comparable to the standard C40 concrete mix. Products are currently being tested for fire resistance, and have an expected life of at least 50 years under normal conditions. The robotic system, as illustrated in Figure 4.30, has the advantage that it can be used at any location including hazardous areas which could not be safely accessed by a human workforce.

The largest 3D-printed structure in the UK to date is the staircase elements of the pedestrian bridge across the M8 at Sighthill, Glasgow.[33] The units were manufactured in Nijmegen, Netherlands

Figure 4.30 3D-printing of concrete by Versarien Technology®. Photograph: Arthur Lyons

before transportation to Scotland. The first UK housing development to use 3D Construction Printing (3DCP) is due to be built at Accrington in Lancashire.

The largest 3D-printed building in Europe is a data centre built in Heidelberg, Germany[34] by Heidelberg Materials®. The building, completed in 2023, is 54 m long, 11 m wide and 9 m high. It was built with 100% recyclable materials specially formulated for 3D-printing. The mineral-based product and binder has a footprint of 55% less than standard Portland cement and was used for all the outer walls and inner partitions.

Europe's first 3D-printed school is being built in Lviv, Ukraine, using equipment from COBOD International®, a Danish 3D-printing construction company, based in Copenhagen[35]. The school is due to open in late 2023.

Category 5 Pre-manufacturing of Non-structural Assemblies

Volumetric Pod Assemblies

Pods, such as pre-assembled kitchens and bathrooms (Figures 4.31–4.34) complete with all plumbing and electrical systems can be directly slotted into existing structures. Also included within this category are M&E (Mechanical and Electrical Services) utility cupboards, risers and plant rooms. The units may be built in timber, steel or concrete. Bathroom pods are also manufactured in GRP. Electrical and plumbing services are then connected into the pre-existing structure with standard connections for immediate operation.

Concrete pods may be manufactured with a reinforced base in either standard or lightweight concrete. Walls may be framed with galvanised steel and completed with concrete panels in thicknesses ranging from 40 mm to 120 mm according to

Figure 4.31 En-suite shower room pods in production at Kondor Pods production facility in Hull. Photograph: Courtesy of Kondor Pods Ltd.[36]

Figure 4.33 En-suite shower room pod installed in new-build student accommodation at 'The Grid', Leeds. Photograph: Courtesy of Kondor Pods Ltd.

Figure 4.32 Completed bathroom pods craned onto site at 'Ocean Bowl', Falmouth. Photograph: Courtesy of Kondor Pods Ltd.

project requirements. Embedded conduits can also be incorporated into the concrete sections for the insertion of electrical and plumbing services.

Steel pods incorporate either a reinforced concrete or steel base surmounted by a galvanised steel frame. Walls and ceiling are infilled with steel profile units incorporating thermal and acoustic insulation and gypsum boards. Electrical conduits and plumbing services are built into the wall and ceiling panel units.

A typical bathroom pod for student accommodation will be fitted with a wall-mounted hand basin, a wall-hung dual-flush toilet and a thermostatic shower enclosed by door or curtain. For high-end apartments steel-framed bathroom pods may be fully fitted with porcelain tile finishes.

Kitchen pods are usually customised to clients' requirements with the option to incorporate oven, hob, sink unit, fridge/freezer, microwave, extractor fan, storage cupboards and fitted worktops.

Figure 4.34 Installed kitchen pod. Photograph: Courtesy of Elfin Kitchens Ltd.[37]

Panelised and Linear Sub-assemblies

This category includes non-structural façade assemblies complete with glazing, also cladding and roof units consisting of both supporting structure and finishes. Precast concrete cladding panels are typically manufactured from GRC and Ultra High Performance Fibre Reinforced Concrete[38] (UHPC).

The ten-storey building over Moorgate station in London is currently being constructed by Mace®[39] who will be using significant off-site solutions. The traditional steel frame (Figure 4.35) will be clad with precast concrete panels, fully factory assembled with aluminium-framed double-glazing units. The building is to be diesel-free in construction and fossil-fuel free in operation using air-source heat pumps and photovoltaic panels. The building will provide eight floors of office space together with retail spaces, outdoor areas and a roof terrace.

Figure 4.35 Structural steelwork at 101 Moorgate, London, prior to the installation of off-site manufactured precast concrete panels. Photograph: Arthur Lyons

Figure 4.36 Smart roof system installed at Bellway Homes[40] development in Leicestershire. Photograph: Courtesy of Bellway Homes

Smart roofs (Figure 4.36) incorporate insulated panels, spandrels, soffit and fascia, also where required, dormers, GRP chimneys, and roof windows. Brickwork assemblies include chimneys, balconies and decorative panels. Smaller units include the wide range of M&E (Mechanical and Electrical Services) assemblies. Category 5 covers fully serviced floor and partition cassettes also pre-assembled cabling and plumbing systems ready for immediate installation and connection. Doorsets when pre-hung and fully finished with architectural ironmongery fall within this category.

References

1. *Modern Methods of Construction – Introducing the MMC Definition Framework*, Website: MMC-I-Pad-base_GOVUK-FINAL_SECURE.pdf (https://www.cast-consultancy.com).
2. *Pre-manufactured Value (PMV). The percentage measure of a construction project's costs derived from pre-delivery to the site* (https://www.cast-consultancy.com).
3. Tide Construction Ltd. (https://tideconstruction.co.uk), London.
4. Ilke Homes Ltd. (https://ilkehomes.co.uk), Knaresborough, North Yorkshire.
5. ModPods International (https://modpodsinternational.com), Coventry.

6. Zed Pods Ltd. (https://zedpods.com), London.

7. Rollforming Services Ltd. (https://www.rollforming.co.nz), Auckland, New Zealand.

8. Urban Splash (https://urbansplash.co.uk), Greater Manchester.

9. inHAUS Prefabricated Concrete Houses, (https://casasinhaus.com), Valencia, Spain.

10. MechSlip Cladding Systems (https://www.mechslip.co.uk), West Bromwich.

11. Ibstock Brick (https://www.ibstockbrick.co.uk), Ibstock, Leicestershire.

12. Vision Modular Systems UK Ltd. (https://visionmodular.com), Bedford.

13. *What is Passivhaus? The gold standard in energy efficiency*, 25 July 2022, Energy Saving Trust, London.

14. Portakabin UK (https://www.portakabin.com), York.

15. *New platform-based approach to construction unveiled* – Seismic® modules - McAvoy, March 2022, Lisburn, Co. Antrim.

16. *Brickwork and Modern Methods of Construction* Brick Development Association, April 2023. The Building Centre, London.

17. Greencore Homes (https://greencorehomes,co.uk), Bicester.

18. *Springfield Meadows – Greencore Construction*, Structural Timber Magazine, Radar Communications Ltd., Shrewsbury, 2023.

19. Stora Enso (https://storaenso.com/en/), Stockholm, Sweden.

20. Vision Development South, (https://www.timber-frame-supplier.co.uk), Reading.

21. *What is cross wall construction? Features and benefits*, 1 June 2019, The Constructor (https://theconstructor.org/construction/cross-wall-construction-features-benefits/33980), San Diego, USA.

22. H+H UK Ltd. (https://www.hhcelcon.co.uk), Sevenoaks, Kent.

23. Specwall SP Ltd. (https://www.specwall.com), Manchester.

24. *Laboratory testing of a novel M-Frame precast beam to beam moment resisting connection*, Riedel, K., Vella, J.P., Rust, G. et al., June 2021, Conference Paper 352478598, ResearchGate Gmbh, Berlin.

25. *D-Frame solution wins second industry accolade*, 29 November 2019, Construction News, London.

26. Nexus Modular (https://nexusmodular.co.uk), Buckhurst Hill, Essex.

27. Hiltongrove (https://www.hiltongrove.co.uk), London.

28. Modular Building Automation (https://www.modularbuildingautomation.eu), Sneek, Netherlands.

29. Mirreco (https://mirreco.com), West Australia.

30. *Minimass 3D-printed concrete beam* (https://ukgbc.org), UK Green Building Council, London.

31. *The 3D printing building construction market is expected to grow at a 169% rate with the rise in construction projects*, 28 September 2022, The Business Research Company, Leicester.

32. *25% of Dubai buildings will be 3D printed by 2030*, 15 May 2021, Arch20, Blacksburg, Virginia, USA.

33. *UK's largest 3D-printed structure opens in Glasgow*, Lago, C., 28 March 2023 (https://constructionmanagement.co.uk), Construction Management Magazine, London.

34. *3D-printed data center being built in Germany* (https://www.datacentredynamics.com), Data Center Dynamics, Heidelberg, Germany.

35. *Europe's first 3D-printed school takes shape in Ukraine* (https://www.rferl.org/), Prague, Czech Republic.

36. Kondor Pods (www.kondor-pods.com), Hull.

37. Elfin Kitchens Ltd. (https://elfinkitchens.co.uk), Colchester.

38. *Everything you need to know about ultra-high performance fibre reinforced concrete* (https://fehrgroup.com/en/cladding-panels/), FEHR, Reichshoffen, France.

39. Mace Group (https://macegroup.com), London.

40. Bellway Homes (https://bellway.co.uk), Newcastle-upon-Tyne.

CHAPTER 5

On-Site Modern Methods of Construction

CONTENTS

Introduction

The two on-site categories of Modern Methods of Construction which lead to enhanced productivity and site labour reduction are described with typical examples.[1]

Category 6 Traditional Building Product Enhancement

This category encompasses the use of large building components rather than the traditional small units in order to increase on-site productivity. Materials include larger than standard external and internal wall units and large format roofing finishes. Large format blockwork is included within this category. Easy-to-install components such as brick slip systems, flexible pipework and pre-fabricated concrete reinforcement also offer enhanced productivity on site.

Large Format Concrete Blockwork

Large format concrete blockwork systems (Figure 5.1) offer a speedier form of

DOI: 10.1201/9781003360469-5

Figure 5.1 Large format aircrete Celcon Plus Block® rapid construction. Photograph: Courtesy of H+H UK Ltd[3]

construction compared to traditional masonry construction using either brick or standard concrete block. Large format blocks manufactured from autoclaved aerated concrete are made to a range of standard sizes including 620 × 430 mm, 620 × 215 mm, 630 × 250 mm and 440 × 430 mm. Thicknesses are typically 100 mm, 140 mm, 150 mm, 200 mm, 215 mm, 275 mm and 300 mm. Compressive strengths range from 2.9 N/mm^2 to 8.7 N/mm^2 giving typical thermal conductivities from $\lambda = 0.11$ W/mK to $\lambda = 0.18$ W/mK. Large format blockwork is suitable for internal and external leafs of cavity construction and also for solid walls. Separating walls can also be constructed with the denser blocks only, as the lighter blocks do not give the necessary acoustic insulation. Also not all large format blocks are suitable for use in beam and block floor construction, but they can be used below ground level.

Large format blockwork is usually constructed using 2 mm thin mortar joint technology, although standard 10 mm joints are also possible. Large format blockwork can offer up to 4 hours of fire resistance with a Class 1 classification.[2] Aerated large format blockwork, when jointed with fully filled thin joints, can provide an individual leakage rate as low as 0.12m^3/hr/m^2@50 Pa, but total building leakage rates are highly dependent on the construction as a whole.

For cavity construction the system allows for the post-fixing of cavity ties, which gives flexibility to the timing for erection of the outer leaf. The fast-setting mortar, which can be applied at relatively low temperatures, allows continuous laying of blockwork up to one storey height and the early addition of floors or roofs. An initial bond is formed within 15 minutes and structural loading is possible after 1–2 hours. During construction, walls should be propped to prevent failure due to excessive wind.

All masonry requires detailing to accommodate drying shrinkage and movement. Generally walls longer than 6 m in length should have movement joints, and the first joint from a corner should be within 3 m. Also movement joints are appropriate where blockwork abuts other structural elements such as steel or reinforced concrete. Stainless steel bed-joint reinforcement is used where crack control is necessary.

The standard finishes are plaster skim for the internal leaf of cavity construction and render externally. Internally a PVA bonding coat is applied before the application of plaster as the blockwork is relatively smooth. Similarly, externally either a stipple coat or metal laths are applied to ensure good bonding of the render finish. Alternatively, as large format thin joint mortar blockwork has a good surface, a thin plaster spray coat of 3–4 mm may be an appropriate finish.

Preformed and In-Situ Insulated Concrete Formwork Systems

Insulated concrete formwork (ICF) systems offer a method for creating structural walls and floors of cast in-situ concrete, using insulating materials that are designed to remain in place as permanent formwork.

A common form of the ICF construction system consists of hollow lightweight blocks (Figure 5.2), consisting of two outer layers of insulating polystyrene or woodcrete connected with a web of steel or recycled plastic. The units are stacked, additional steel reinforcement inserted as required, and the void filled with concrete. Externally the insulation can be rendered or clad in brick, tile, stone or timber. Internally, plasterboard is the standard finish. A variety of products offer U-values in the range 0.30–0.11 W/m^2K. The basic system has been in use for many years, but it is still considered to be a modern method of construction.

Other systems use large format insulating panels which can be assembled on or off site for craning into position ready to be filled with concrete. Using this process Panelox®[4] can build from foundation to roof plate level a standard house within three working days. The woodchip panels provide the internal and external wall surfaces between which are sandwiched insulation and a poured concrete core. The U-value, depending upon the inserted insulation, can be as low as 0.09 W/m^2K. The woodchip panels made from 90% recycled wood are mineralised against fire, humidity, mould and rodent damage. ICF walls are typically characterised by high levels of airtightness, good insulation and low thermal bridging.

Monolithic Clay Block Construction

On site masonry can be constructed quickly using the single block construction SmartWall®[5] system which removes the requirement for cavities. Large fired aerated clay blocks with thermal conductivity in the range $\lambda = 0.06–0.09$ W/mK are manufactured in a wide range of thickness. The 300 mm block has a U-value of

Figure 5.2 Insulating concrete formwork (ICF). Photograph: Arthur Lyons

0.28 W/m²K, and the largest unit at 500 mm has a U-value of 0.11 W/m²K. The system offers speedy construction as no cavity is required, removing the requirement for added insulation or the insertion of wall ties. Blocks are laid with full width thin joint adhesive to a thickness of 1.0 mm with a roller applicator. No mortar is required in the interlocking vertical joints as the blocks are manufactured to a tolerance of 1.0 mm. The construction requires no additional concrete or steel reinforcement and no propping is required during the construction process. Additionally as little moisture is used in the building process and construction time is reduced, the building can be roofed and weathertight in a greatly reduced time.

Air tightness of the construction is achieved by a plaster finish on the interior. The standard exterior finish is a vapour-permeable render. The clay blockwork gives thermal mass to stabilise temperatures and reduce overheating in summer. Additional thermal insulation can be achieved by the use of the filled blocks which incorporate rock wool insulation or polystyrene (EPS) beads which are expanded by steam to fully fill the cavities within the blocks. Corner and window reveal blocks are standard and lintels are formed from a combination of steel box units and uninsulated or insulated U-blocks. Blocks can be cut on site as required using a masonry saw.

An alternative mortar bonding system uses mortar pads. The first line of blockwork is moistened and the specialist mortar pads are laid across the full block width, cutting and adjusting as necessary. The mortar pads are then moistened and the next course of blocks laid and aligned. A further alternative system is the use of very strong PU (polyurethane) adhesive which is sprayed along the two edges of the blockwork, rather than the full width when using standard thin coat mortar adhesive from a roller applicator. The first course of blockwork must be laid on a carefully level and even base to ensure subsequent accuracy in the build.

Category 7 On-Site Labour Reduction and Productivity Enhancement

This category incorporates the use of all the latest electronic technologies to enhance output. These include the use of BIM (Building Information Modelling) and AI to enhance workflow efficiency, GPS (Global Positioning System) as a planning tool, AR/VR (Augmented Reality / Virtual Reality), robotics and drones for assisting site work. When AR and VR are combined, additional digital elements can be brought into the virtual world in real time,

all fully integrated with modelling systems such as AutoCAD®[6] and Revit® to millimetre accuracy. The technology can assist in the detection of potential problematic clashes.

Robotics systems include the on-site production of construction site layouts using the HP SitePrint®[7] robot (Figure 5.3) and the Q-bot®[8] robot (Figure 5.4) to spray foam insulation onto the underside of suspended floors subject to a successful survey and suitable access.

One example of productivity enhancement is the use of tunnel form which is a formwork system that allows the contractor to cast walls and slabs in one operation. Although dating back many years, it is recognised as a modern method of construction as it offers the speed and quality of off-site production with the economy of standard on-site concrete placement procedure. The demountable formwork is essentially a series of open-ended upturned U-shaped units which are placed at the correct distance apart to allow in-situ concrete to be poured in the gap making the vertical walls. Reinforcement is then laid across the whole and the upper floor slab concrete poured, so that walls and floors are effectively cast together as a monolithic structure. Surface finishes are good, so no subsequent plastering or finishing is required. The process can be repeated on a 24 hour cycle as heating can be applied within the cells to ensure sufficient setting and hardening overnight. Tunnel form construction is particularly appropriate for construction of repetitive cellular structures such as student accommodation, hotels and commercial developments.[8]

Figure 5.3 HP SitePrint® robot for on-site construction site layout production. Photograph: Arthur Lyons

Figure 5.4 Q-bot® robot to spray the underside of suspended floors with insulation material. Photograph: Arthur Lyons.

The use of robotic bricklaying[9] which is described in Chapter 10 – Masonry and Alternative Units page 82 is a recent labour saving development. The system works from digitised architects' plans and can complete the masonry structure of a house in about two weeks. Other enhancements include using insulated concrete formwork which eliminates time consumed in setting up and removing temporary works.

Site encapsulation for weather protection can save considerable time wastage and damage to exposed construction materials.

References

1. *Modern Methods of Construction – Introducing the MMC Definition Framework*, Website: MMC-I-Pad-base_GOVUK-FINAL_SECURE.pdf, (https://www.cast-consultancy.com).

2. British Standard BS 476 Part 7. *Fire tests on building materials and structures – Method of test to determine the classification of the surface spread of flame of products.* 15 January 1997, BSI, London.

3. H+H UK Ltd., (https://www.hhcelcon.co.uk), Sevenoaks, Kent.

4. Panelox Systems Ltd., (https://panelox.co.uk), Alton, Hampshire.

5. Juwo Evolved SmartWall Ltd., (https://juwo-smartwall.co.uk), Bodmin, Cornwall.

6. AutoCAD Revit, (https://www.autodesk.co.uk), San Francisco, USA.

7. HP SitePrint – Hewlett-Packard Development Company, (https://www.hp.com/us-en/printers/site-print/layout-robot.html), Palo Alto, California.

8. Q-bot Ltd., (https://q-bot.co), London.

9. *UK's first home built by robot bricklayer*, Morby, A., 6 October 2020, Construction Enquirer, London.

CHAPTER 6

Transportation and Installation

CONTENTS

Introduction

Where large building units are to be constructed off-site, the anticipated methods of transportation and craning of the units on-site are critical early design considerations, especially in relation to tight urban sites.

Factory to Site Transportation

Modular construction greatly reduces the number of traffic movements around individual building sites, but requires large heavy transport for the delivery of modules. The standard in-factory procedure was lifting the units by crane or hoist onto the delivery vehicles. However, the alternative Totalkare® system[1] uses a set of column lifts which allow the volumetric modules to be raised in the factory so that flat-bed transport can be reversed underneath, prior to lowering and securing the units for transportation.

Figures 6.1 and 6.2 respectively illustrate the necessary transport required for delivery of large roof units and multiple pods to building sites.

DOI: 10.1201/9781003360469-6

Figure 6.1 Transportation of multiple roof modules. Photograph: Courtesy of BOS Logistica[2]

Figure 6.2 Completed bathroom units delivered to 'Ocean Bowl', Falmouth site by East Riding Transport. Photograph: Courtesy of Kondor Pods Ltd.[3]

Installation of Modular Units

On site, mobile or tower cranes are used for lifting and accurate placing of the modular units. Many tight urban sites, such as the illustrated 'Chapter' building at Lewisham (Figure 6.3), only have very limited access, and early detailed planning is vital to ensure successful site operations.

For smaller units, a crane truck, as illustrated in Figure 6.4, is appropriate and easily manoeuvred.

Figure 6.3 Tower crane installation of modular units at 'Chapter', Lewisham, London. Photograph: Courtesy of Weston Williamson + Partners

Figure 6.4 Crane truck offloading modular unit. Photograph: Courtesy of Rise Adaptations[4] and IMA Architects

References

1. Totalkare Ltd. (https://totalkare.co.uk), Kingswinford, Dudley, West Midlands.
2. BOS Logistica Ltd. (https://boslogistic.co.uk), Middlewich, Cheshire.
3. East Riding Transport Ltd. (https://ertl.co.uk), Hull, East Yorkshire.
4. Rise Adaptations Ltd. (https://riseadapt.co.uk), Doncaster, South Yorkshire.

CHAPTER 7

Foundations

CONTENTS

Introduction

Permanent foundations for modular building may be of traditional form or pre-manufactured to reduce on-site time and labour. The form of foundation is dependent on the generic type of module system, whether the loading is transferred through vertical walls or by way of edge beams to corner support.[1] Foundations for temporary or semi-permanent modular buildings may be recyclable supporting units on a stabilised base rather than traditional poured concrete.

Types of Foundation

Poured concrete or reinforced concrete is the standard foundation material for permanent low-rise modular construction. In addition, one or two courses of blockwork may also be required. The skirting detail for wooden modular units requires particular attention to prevent timber degradation. Appropriate foundations are normally designed and specified by the manufacturer of the volumetric units, as fixing to the foundation is specific to the particular module. Foundations will include all the servicing required for connection with the installed module. This will include storm and domestic drains, electrical supply and telecommunication systems. Connection to a gas supply is not normally required as it is being phased out to comply with the building regulations which require no gas main connections from 2025 for new build.

Pre-manufactured foundations are classified as Category 3 in Modern Methods of Construction according to the MHCLG framework[2] thus increasing the pre-manufactured value[3] (PMV) of the overall project. The RBeam® system[4] (Figure 7.1) is essentially a kit of parts consisting of pre-manufactured piles, caps and beams in

DOI: 10.1201/9781003360469-7

Figure 7.1 RBeam® precast ground beam foundation system. Photograph: Courtesy of Roger Bullivant Ltd.

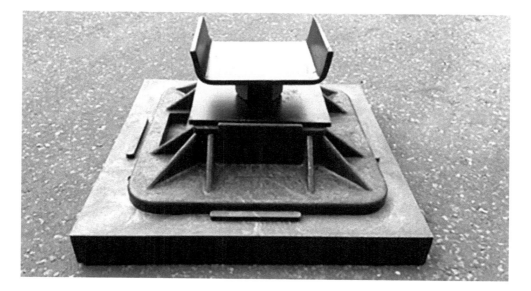

Figure 7.2 Jackpad® foundation system for semi-permanent and portable modular buildings. Photograph: Courtesy of Jackpad Ltd.

Figure 7.3 Jackpad® foundation system installed under a new modular building. Photograph: Courtesy of Jackpad Ltd.

low-carbon concrete which can be installed speedily to ensure minimal on-site construction time and disturbance. The system is flexible to be adjusted to the relevant soil types and conditions. A wide range of beam sizes and lengths are standard and the system is appropriate for use in buildings up to four storeys in height.

The foundations for temporary or semi-permanent modular construction range from concrete strip or precast concrete pads to blockwork. Where it is anticipated that the building will be moved within a medium or relatively short timescale then Jackpads®[5] (Figures 7.2 and 7.3) on a stabilised base offer an appropriate solution. The units comprise a load-spreading base manufactured from recycled plastic which rests on a plastic sub-base. The built modular construction is then supported on a fully adjustable steel unit. The whole support system can easily be relocated as required.

References

1. *Design and Construction of high-rise modular buildings based on recent projects*, Hough, M.H. and Lawson, R.M. Proc. Institution of Civil Engineers, Vol. 172, Issue 6, pp. 37–44, November 2019, ICE Publishing, London.

2. *Modern Methods of Construction – Introducing the MMC Definition Framework*, Website: MMC-I-Padbase_GOVUK-FINAL_SECURE.pdf (https://www.cast-consultancy.com).

3. *Premanufactured Value (PMV). The percentage measure of a construction project's* costs derived from pre-delivery to the site (https://www.cast-consultancy.com).

4. *RBeam – Precast ground beam system* (https://roger-bullivant.co.uk), Swadlingcote, Derbyshire.

5. Jackpad Ltd. (https://jackpad.co.uk), Fleckney, Leicestershire.

CHAPTER 8

Fire

CONTENTS

Introduction

Since the disastrous London Grenfell Tower[1] fire in 2017, fire spread has been high on the agenda, particularly in relation to medium and high-rise buildings and the use of timber. It is now suggested by a consortium of 24 insurers[2] that multi-storey mass timber buildings should have a concrete core and lower levels to allay insurers' concerns about potential fire and water damage. Clearly constructing with timber is vital to meet the 2050 net-zero obligations, but equally, the use of hybrid construction is a pragmatic approach to resolving the issue of fire risk whilst still delivering on reduced embodied carbon levels.

Fire Safety

The UK's Building Regulations set the requirements for ensuring safety in the home and all workplaces. The criteria is that any building should remain structurally stable and with safe egress until complete evacuation has taken place or all occupants are in a place of safety. But building insurers require an analysis of how the building will be after the fire is extinguished and how much water damage can be expected as this significantly affects potential reinstatement costs. However, it is worth noting that more damage and financial loss is accrued by the accidental escape of water rather than fire and this has a bearing on the use of engineered timber products which may delaminate when exposed long-term to hidden water seepage. In terms of risk, the spread of unnoticed fire through building voids and cavities is considered by building insurers as a major challenge. This problem is particularly relevant to rear-ventilated

DOI: 10.1201/9781003360469-8

facades where fire can spread rapidly if materials do not comply with at least a Euroclass A2-s1,d0[3] fire classification to BS EN 13501-1:2018.[4]

From the insurers' perspective, ideally at least half the structure of multi-storey buildings should be non-combustible. One way is to alternate timber with concrete in construction. High-risk areas such as kitchens, plant rooms and other heavily electrically serviced facilities should be located on concrete floors or within the concrete core to give greater compartmentation.

Enhanced reaction-to-fire performance for wood-based products can be achieved by the use of fire retardants. Many timbers can be treated to achieve a B-s1,d0 fire rating to BS EN 13501:2018. Internally, timber frame, structural insulated panel (SIPs) and solid wood forms of construction can achieve appropriate fire protection with plasterboard or similar non-combustible materials. However, building developers must take fire and water damage risks into consideration at the design stage. Table 8.1 lists the classes of reaction to fire performance for internal wood products except floorings.

Following the Grenfell Tower disaster, the Building Regulations Approved Document B (fire safety)[5] – (England) was amended in 2020 and 2022. The main change was a ban on combustible materials on exterior walls and roofs to prevent external fire spread over the walls and from one building to another. The legal requirement is that external walls should comply with the European classification A1 or A2-s1,d0, for buildings over 11m in height which contain one or more dwelling, an institution or a room for residential purposes. The same fire prevention requirements apply to buildings other than dwellings.

Table 8.1 Classes of reaction to fire performance for wood products except flooring

Product	Minimum thickness (mm)	Class (excluding floorings)
Cement-bonded particleboard	10	B-s1,d0
Hardboard	6	D-s2,d0
Wood-based panels	18	D-s2,d0
Solid-wood panelling and cladding	18	D-s2,d0
Wood-based panels	3	E
Fibreboard, soft	9	E
Structural timber	22	D-s2,d0
Glued-laminated timber (Glulam)	40	D-s2,d0
Cross-laminated timber (CLT) (Lamella 18mm minimum)	54	D-s2,d0
Laminated veneer lumber (Veneer 3mm minimum)	18	D-s2,d0

Notes: A1 = non-combustible materials, A2 = non-combustible (Scotland) and limited combustibility (England and Wales).
B, C and D ranges from very limited to medium contribution to fire. E and F are high contribution to fire.
S refers to the level of smoke emitted within the first ten minutes of exposure to fire. S1 = little or no smoke, s2 = quite a lot of smoke, s3 = substantial/heavy smoke.
d refers to flaming droplets. d0 = no droplets, d1 = some droplets, d2 = quite a lot of droplets.
Data from Timber Industry website- 'Fire Safety – Wood in Construction', (https://timberfiresafety.org), 3 March 2023, Produced by Swedish Wood, Timber Development UK (TDUK) and Structural Timber Association (STA).

References

1. Grenfell Tower: 24 Storey tower block fire in London which led to the deaths of 72 residents in 2017.
2. *Insurance challenges of massive timber construction and a possible way forward.* Fire Protection Association (FPA): Revision 1.0, January 2022, Williams, D., RISC Authority. Also response by Glocking, J., FPA & RISC Authority, 27 April 2022.
3. European Reaction to Fire classification (EuroClass) A1 – non-combustible, A2 – limited combustibility.
4. British Standard BS EN 13501-1:2018. *Fire classification of construction products and building elements. Classification using data from reaction to fire tests.* BSI, London.
5. Building Regulations 2010, Approved Document B (fire safety):
   Volume 1: Dwellings, 2019 edition incorporating 2020 and 2022 amendments – for use in England.
   Volume 2: Buildings other than dwellings, 2019 edition incorporating 2020 and 2022 amendments – for use in England.

CHAPTER 9

Innovative Materials – Introduction

CONTENTS

Introduction

The built environment is a major producer of carbon emissions, and this has to be addressed to comply with the UK commitment of achieving net zero carbon emissions by 2050 and a target of 50% reduction by 2030. Overall, the built environment contributes to approximately 40% of global emissions. The energy associated with buildings is divided between that consumed in construction and that used in lifetime operations. The embodied energy associated with construction includes the extraction of minerals, material manufacture and transportation, the construction process, in-use refurbishment and ultimate end-of-life disposal. In relation to embodied energy, many manufacturers provide Environmental Product Declarations[1] (EPDs) giving data on the environmental impact of their products. Table 9.1 lists the four key stages in the full life cycle of construction products according to the British Standard BS EN 15804: 2012 + A2: 2019.[2] The EPD must be verifiable and consistent based on a full life cycle assessment. The first three stages of the EPD are within the sphere of 'Cradle to Gate'. For 'Cradle to Grave' the disposal stage is included. Only if no carbon emissions are made in the 'Cradle to Gate' stages and the material is taken from one building and reused can this be reasonably described as 'Cradle to Cradle'. The latter is fairly rare as some energy and transportation are normal during a reuse process.

The challenge to the material manufacturers is to significantly reduce their carbon footprint and this applies especially to steel, concrete, aluminium and glass

DOI: 10.1201/9781003360469-9

Table 9.1 Sustainability of construction works – Environmental Product Declarations (EPDs) – Core rules for the product category of construction products to BS EN 15804: 2012 + A2: 2019

Product Stage

A1   Raw material extraction

A2   Transport from extraction site to manufacturer

A3   Manufacture and fabrication

Construction Process Stage

A4   Transportation to building site

A5   Construction and installation on site

Use Stage

B1   Use

B2   Maintenance

B3   Repair

B4   Replacement

B5   Refurbishment

B6   Operational energy

B7   Operational water

End-of-Life Stage

C1   Deconstruction and demolition

C2   Transport to recycling facility

C3   Waste processing

C4   Disposal

Reuse, Recovery and Recycling Benefits

D   Reuse, recovery and recycling

which are the major carbon emitters related to the building industry. While new eco-friendly materials are emerging, it is inevitable that the traditional construction materials, will for some time, remain the key elements of building. This text

therefore describes the changes that are being made to traditional material manufacture and composition as well as illustrating new alternatives. The current standard manufacturing processes and product descriptions are not included as they are fully described in alternative texts including *Materials for Architects and Builders*.[3]

Sustainability has been on the agenda for many years but its profile has been raised, particularly in the post-Covid era, and is supported by the potential development of many innovative construction materials. Some novel materials, although they have great potential, may never be adopted to any significant extent in the building industry, which tends for understandable financial reasons, to be rather conservative. However, these potential materials are included within the text as their future uptake is partially dependent on the awareness of their existence. Also, often it is not clear at first, how novel materials might be utilised and subsequently become the norm within construction.

This section on Innovative Materials therefore includes a wide range of emergent materials, only a proportion of which are likely to become routine construction materials in the near future. Many emergent materials are untested and their inclusion in this text only suggests their potential, but does not guarantee their performance within construction. The information included in this text is based entirely on manufacturers' published data and has not been verified by the author. Many new materials are not yet supported by a British Standard or British Board of Agrément (BBA) certification. Specifiers must refer directly to the manufacturers and their detailed technical information to ensure that any new materials are appropriate to their proposed application.

References

1. Environmental Product Declarations – A document that quantifiably demonstrates the environmental impact of a product based on a verified full life-cycle assessment according to the British Standard BS EN 15804 (https://wwwenvirondec.com/home), The International EPD System, Stockholm, Sweden.

2. British Standard. BS EN 15804: 2012 + A2: 2019, *Sustainability of Construction Works – Environmental Product Declarations. Core rules for the product category of construction products.* BSI, London.

3. *Materials for Architects and Builders*, Arthur Lyons, 6th edition, 2020, Routledge, Abingdon, Oxfordshire.

CHAPTER 10

Masonry and Alternative Units

CONTENTS

Introduction

This chapter initially deals with the problems facing the traditional clay and concrete masonry unit manufacturers as they strive to achieve zero carbon by 2050. The immediate approach is to maximise current efficiency and reduce emissions by blending fuels. However, the longer-term objective necessarily is to change completely to zero-carbon fuels. Whilst alternative building materials are appearing in the market, there is no realistic expectation that the traditional materials – fired bricks to BS EN 771-1: 2011 + A1: 2015[1] and cast concrete

DOI: 10.1201/9781003360469-10

blocks – will totally disappear from the construction industry.

The latter part of the chapter describes the main alternatives to traditional brick and block which are either currently available or under well-developing research. Clearly some materials will remain only as a niche market, but others such as hempcrete are likely to become serious contenders within the construction industry as their availability and distribution systems evolve.

Low Carbon Clay Bricks

The spiralling cost of gas together with environmental concerns is driving the brick-making industry to reconsider its energy requirements. Necessarily brick manufacture is energy intensive requiring high-temperature kilns, typically fired by natural gas at around 1050°C. Hydrogen is recognised as the future key technology for the industry, but this is dependent on the roll-out of a national infrastructure giving a secure supply.

An alternative approach is being taken by the brick company Michelmersh® in Belgium which is investing in solar energy. It is anticipated that half the energy requirement of the brick factory at Floren will be solar by 2023.[2] The company's three other factories, located in the UK, are also investing in solar power to mitigate the soaring cost and potential disruptions of natural gas supply.

Necessarily, water is used in traditional brick manufacture, and the industry is reducing the quantity of mains supplied water by using rainwater collected in quarries. Overall 71% of water now used by the industry is sourced from non-mains supply.[3]

Clay is the principal material used in brick manufacture, but approximately 6% of alternative materials (Materials from Alternative, Recycled and Secondary Sources – MARSS) are now used in brick production, ensuring resource-efficient use of natural clays. Inevitably some waste material is generated in brick production, but 95% of this is recycled and only a small proportion of hazardous waste is sent to landfill sites. No fired brick waste is sent to landfill as it can be re-purposed. The brick and block industry is actively collaborating with the ready mix and precast concrete sectors on sustainability including ways of reducing plastic packaging.

The majority of clay brick manufacturers own and manage their quarries. Necessarily extraction of clay affects the local environment, but now the majority of landowners are making considerable efforts to restore the sites after extraction and to enhance wildlife and biodiversity both in the active extraction sites and where restoration has taken place.[3]

Low Carbon Concrete Bricks

In one project, Marshalls® are using the CarbonCure Technologies® system to inject carbon dioxide into its concrete-facing bricks to remove it from the environment. The CO_2 to be used initially is the waste product from the fertiliser industry. It is claimed[4] that concrete bricks have 50% less embodied energy than clay bricks. In an alternative project, the company is researching the manufacture of its concrete bricks using zero cement content.

Low Embodied Energy Bricks

Low embodied energy bricks (K-briq®) (Figures 10.1 and 10.2) are manufactured from over 90% recycled construction and demolition waste together with recycled gypsum and a binder.[5] The bricks are formed like traditional clay bricks but are not fired and the process incorporates only 5% of the embodied energy compared to traditional brick production. The bricks can be used as an alternative to clay or concrete bricks, subject to pending certification by the BBA (British Board of Agrément). At end-of-life, the bricks can be recycled into new low-energy bricks. The technical specifications of strength and thermal mass are similar to traditional bricks. A range of thirteen stock colours

incorporating recycled pigments and colour matching to existing traditional brickwork is available. The manufacture of bricks from recycled material eliminates the need for further quarrying of clay with its associated environmental effects.

Hemp Bricks

Hemp bricks (Figure 10.3) are one of a range of hemp products from Mirreco® Hemp CAST® (Carbon Asset Storage Technology) which are under development in Australia. Mirreco, in conjunction with Curtin University Perth, is developing a range of carbon-neutral building products based on hemp blended with natural polymers. Current research includes accreditation testing to Australian, British, ASTM and ISO international technical standards. Further pending products include panels, beams, sprayed composites, insulation and 3D-printing.

Figure 10.1 K-briq® – Brick manufactured from recycled waste. Photograph: Arthur Lyons

Figure 10.2 Panel illustrating the K-briq® colour range. Photograph: Arthur Lyons

Recycled Ceramic Waste Bricks

Green Leaf® bricks in the USA[6] are manufactured from 100% recycled materials, mainly ceramic waste, but including some clay, industrial filter waste and wastewater solids. Between 15% and 31% of the materials are from post-consumer streams. The pre-consumer materials are largely manufacturing and mining waste. The standard perforated brick forms are kiln fired by natural gas. Red, black and brown colours are produced. The bricks are produced in the state of North Carolina.

Figure 10.3 Hemp bricks. Photograph: Courtesy of MirrecoHempCAST®, West Australia

Biological Cement Bricks

The company bioMason® has developed a technology that uses bacteria to form cementitious material to bind fine aggregate into durable brick forms.[7] Sand in brick moulds is inoculated with bacteria which encapsulate the grains initiating the growth of calcium carbonate crystals. Nutrient-rich water is fed into the moulds to accelerate the process, which fills the gaps between the grains of sand. After four days the bricks can be removed from the moulds and used in construction. The process is called microbial-induced calcite precipitation and the product can be as strong as marble. One disadvantage of the process is that it produces ammonia, which the micro-organisms convert into nitrates as a potential pollutant to groundwater.

The technology used by Prometheus® to produce concrete involves the bio-mineralization of calcium carbonate with microalgae.[8] The process produces up to 90% less carbon dioxide compared to standard Portland cement-based concrete and the majority of the water used in the process evaporates into the atmosphere. The concrete produced has physical properties equivalent to standard material as illustrated by the concrete building block (Figure 10.4).

Wool Bricks

Wool bricks[9] are manufactured by blending sheep's wool into standard brick-making clay, followed by the addition of alginate which is extracted from the cell walls of seaweed. The bricks are dried naturally which prevents cracking or distortion. The product is stronger than unfired stabilised earth bricks. The wool can be repurposed waste from textile manufacturers rather than new material.

Figure 10.4 Prometheus® biomineralized concrete block. Photograph: Arthur Lyons

Smart Bricks

Washington University in St. Louis is researching the potential for brick walls to store limited quantities of electricity.[10] The university has patented a process for converting the red pigment in common bricks into a plastic that conducts electricity, making the bricks act as supercapacitors. It is claimed that about 60 standard red bricks could store enough energy to run emergency lighting for 50 minutes. Recharging from a solar system would take 13 minutes.

The process involves treating the bricks with acid vapour to dissolve the red iron oxide, followed by reacting the active iron with a sulphur compound which coats the pores in the brick with an electrically conductive plastic [poly (3,4 Ethylenedioxythiophene) PEDOT] nanofibre layer. The research continues to determine commercial viability.

Unfired Clay Bricks and Blocks

Unfired clay bricks and blocks[11] are manufactured from clay and may incorporate straw and other materials. When mixed with other components such as lime or cement these bricks and blocks are frequently referred to as Stabilised Compressed Earth Blocks (SCEBs). Traditional clay bricks were made by hand giving variability in the product, but modern machine moulded unfired clay bricks are produced to narrow tolerances using the standard brick manufacturing extrusion or pressing processes. The bricks are air dried to reduce shrinkage. Unfired clay bricks have only 14% of the embodied energy associated with the equivalent fired brick.

Unfired clay bricks are suitable for internal walls, but not for high-load structural applications. Sodium silicate or lignosulphonate-stabilised clay-based mortars are usually necessary for their added strength over natural clay or lime-based mortar. The standard sodium silicate mortar has less than 10% of the embodied energy of most cement-based mortars. Unfired clay bricks should be protected from rain and moisture on site and only used above damp-proof course or damp-proof membrane level. The material can be worked on site with standard tools. Off-cuts can be soaked in water and used in landscaping.

Ecoterre® unfired clay bricks[12] are available in two sizes 220 × 105 × 67mm and 220 × 105 × 133mm. Unfired clay bricks can be finished with a variety of breathable materials including clay or lime plasters, limewash and vapour-permeable paints.

Unfired clay blocks (Figure 10.5) have compressive strengths typically in the range of 2.5–5N/mm^2 depending on composition. Manufacturers produce a range of sizes but 100mm is the standard thickness. Blocks may be tongued and grooved or square-edged and are easily cut as required. Unfired clay blockwork is usually finished internally with a skim coat of clay plaster, although it can be painted directly. Walling has the advantage that it is totally recyclable and its hygroscopic property controls the humidity of the internal environment providing that the plaster and paint are vapour-permeable.

Strocks® (425 × 100 × 160 or 210mm) (Figure 10.6) can be used for internal

Figure 10.5 Unfired clay block. Photograph: Courtesy of Ibstock Brick

Figure 10.6 Clay and straw brick – Strocks® manufactured by H.G. Matthews. Photograph: Arthur Lyons

load-bearing walls up to three storeys. They are bonded with the same clay as the blocks creating a homogeneous wall. The equivalent bricks (215 × 65 × 100mm) are made from the same clay and chopped straw material. Strocks have a thermal conductivity λ = 0.2W/mK and compressive strength up to 4.6N/mm².

Sargablocks®, currently specific to Mexico and the Caribbean, are construction blocks manufactured from sargassum seaweed that naturally washes up onto the beaches in that area.[13] The adobe blocks are made from a mix of 40% sargassum and 60% local clay, which is pressed into form and then sun-dried for four hours prior to use. Sargassum blocks are a low-cost building material which has potential in developing countries which have a natural supply of sargassum seaweed washed up every day onto the seashores.

Cob Bricks and Blocks

Cob is made from local clay, some aggregate and straw, whereas unfired clay does not necessarily include straw. Cob bricks and blocks are currently produced in Cornwall using the local clay soil which is being diverted from going into landfill as waste from large-scale construction projects in the area. Only local barley straw is incorporated into the mix. Unlike other natural clay products, no lime or hardeners are included in the blend. The units are air dried to ensure minimal embodied energy. The bricks and blocks are suitable for internal and external applications. Internally a stabilising fluid may be applied to prevent dusting, and externally a water repellent can be used. However, cob walling in high exposure areas requires render for protection.

Standard cob blocks, manufactured by Earth Blocks UK®, are 385 × 215 × 70 or

100mm and 255 × 100 × 70 or 100mm. Standard cob bricks are 255 × 100 × 100mm. A range of matching rounded specials including arch units and brick slips are produced to avoid the need to cut units on site.

Traditional cob construction is being tested for durability and structural strength by the University of Plymouth with a new single-storey building due for completion in 2022.[14] The local clay is blended with hemp rather than straw which was traditionally used. The environmental advantage of cob construction is the total elimination of the use of cement with its associated high embodied energy.

Zero/Low Carbon Concrete Blocks

CarbonNeutral® masonry blocks are manufactured with low carbon materials saving up to 80% on CO_2e. The residual 20% CO_2 is offset by the purchase of carbon credits from projects that deliver immediate emission reductions through sustainable development and renewable energy projects. The offsetting is in accordance with the global CarbonNeutral Protocol.[15] CarbonNeutral® blocks have the same physical properties, including strength and durability, as traditional concrete blocks manufactured with ordinary Portland cement.

Greenbloc® is manufactured to a standard 100 × 440 × 215mm to BS EN 771-3: 2011 + A1: 2015,[16] with a density in the range 1850–2000kg/m³. The 77% reduction in CO_2 compared to traditional CEM1 concrete blocks is achieved by using industrial waste as cementitious materials rather than ordinary Portland cement.

Hollow Concrete Blocks

CarbonBuilt® hollow blocks are manufactured with carbon-sequestering concrete. The basic components are hydrated lime and secondary cementitious materials (SCMs) rather than Portland cement clinker. Hollow concrete blocks are cast by standard industrial processes, followed by curing in a chamber of dilute carbon dioxide and steam at a moderate temperature and under atmospheric pressure. This mineralises approximately 2% of base material to a depth of approximately 50mm, which limits the production process to hollow blocks rather than solid masonry units. The concrete mix may be lightweight or dense but necessarily during the curing process the carbon dioxide/steam mix must circulate freely around the units. The carbon dioxide is obtained from industrial waste, biomass or from direct air capture. The reduction in embodied CO_2 ranges from 70% to 100% depending on the starting materials. With a pure hydrated lime mix, a typical eCO_2 reduction of 82% is achieved. The manufacturers are researching methods to extend the process to larger concrete units.

Hollow Fired Clay Blocks

Hollow perforated fired clay blocks (Figure 10.7) have an interlocking design which removes the requirement for mortar in the vertical joint. The 1mm horizontal

Figure 10.7 Porotherm® large interlocking hollow fired clay blocks. Photograph: Arthur Lyons

joint mortar is applied rapidly with a roller, avoiding waste. The fired clay blocks are highly insulating as they are extruded with a pattern of void spaces and the clay starting material is mixed with sawdust residue which on firing produces a highly porous ceramic product. Completed 365mm blockwork can achieve a U-Value of $0.15W/m^2K$, when finished with 50mm insulation ($\lambda = 0.022W/mK$) and 20mm render externally and a combination of parge, plasterboard and skim (27.5mm) internally.

Hempcrete Blocks

Hempcrete blocks (Figures 10.8 and 10.9) manufactured from hemp and lime (as described in Chapter 11, page 104) are ideal for external wall insulation in timber-framed buildings. Usually, the material is finished externally with render and internally with plaster. Blocks are laid in thin bed lime mortar. Hempcrete blocks can also be used for internal walls and floors. Standard sizes are 500 × 200 × 80, 120 or 300mm. Compressive strength is 0.7MPa and thermal conductivity $\lambda = 0.076W/mK$.

Woodcrete Blocks

Woodcrete Isotex® blocks[17] are manufactured from recycled Spruce softwood mixed with Portland cement. Additives are incorporated to mineralise the wood and to increase moisture and fire resistance. The units are dry-stacked as insulating concrete formwork (ICF) for in-filling with concrete to produce a monolithic structural walling system. A range of forms are produced to offer alternative structural and insulation requirements. The standard block size is 500mm length by 250mm height with

Figure 10.8 Hemp shiv – the chopped woody core of the hemp plant used for making hempcrete. Photograph: Arthur Lyons

widths from 300mm to 440mm. Graphite polystyrene (GPS) insulation is integral within the blocks to give the required U-value which ranges from U = 0.23W/m²K to U = 0.11W/m²K.

An alternative by Durisol ICF® (Figure 10.10) is an interlocking block-work system manufactured from cement-bonded wood waste that requires no mortar when the units are dry-stacked.[18] The insulating concrete formwork pro-duces a single skin external, internal or retaining wall when infilled with con-crete, which may incorporate vertical reinforcement if required. Inserts of insulation, which can be made of PIR

Figure 10.9 Hempcrete block. Photograph: Arthur Lyons

(polyisocyanurate foam), mineral wool or cork, further reduce the thermal conductivity which is similar to timber, rather than concrete, due to the composition of the structural material. Openings can be constructed without a lintel by using rebars within the blockwork. Door openings can be supported during construction with a 'goal post' timber frame. Curved walls may be constructed by cutting blocks with a reciprocating saw. No bracing is normally required during construction work, except for plywood (12–18mm) near to corners, to prevent movement during the concrete pour. Small gaps, over 10mm in width, can be filled with fire-rated foam. Internal finishes are render, plaster or plasterboard on dabs. External finishes range from render and brick slips to stone, timber and rainscreen cladding. Standard block sizes are thicknesses of 170, 250, 300 and 365 × 500mm long and 250mm high.

Figure 10.10 Interlocking block manufactured by Durisol ICF® incorporating polyisocyanurate foam insulation. Photograph: Arthur Lyons

Plastic Waste Bricks and Blocks

Plastic waste blocks manufactured by ByBlock® in the USA are made from 100% recycled plastic material.[19] They are suitable for use in retaining walls, landscaping and feature walls up to a maximum height of 2400mm. Standard blocks are 394 × 197 × 203 and 227mm, weighing 10kg. The standard blocks have interlocking profiles to provide stability and shear strength, but flat top versions (203mm) are available for wall penetrations and for the location of a wall plate. For wall construction, a 10–16mm threaded metal rod is inserted through the preformed hole to bind together adjacent

blocks securely. No adhesives are required between blocks. The material is water and vermin resistant and can be worked with most standard tools. The blocks can be integrated with any other standard building materials. They can be coated with plaster or any standard dry-wall finish. ByBlocks® should not be exposed to fire risk and where appropriate should be clad or treated with fire-retardant materials. Exposure to direct sunlight may cause bleaching of the colours, but no two blocks are the same, due to the variability of the starting material.

Researchers at De Montfort University have developed a 3D-printed brick manufactured from domestic waste including coffee cup lids and plastic bottles[20]

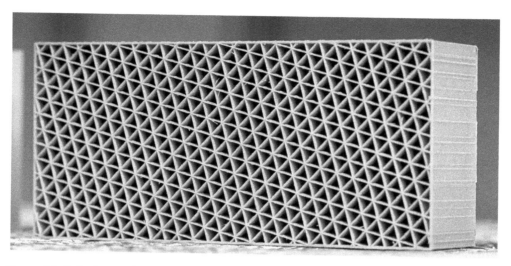

Figure 10.11 Brick manufactured by 3D-printing from recycled domestic plastic waste. Photograph: Courtesy of De Montfort University, Leicester

(Figure 10.11). The brick, which has standard clay brick dimensions, is 3D-printed in the form of a lattice of plastic strips. The grid structure was inspired by the woven construction of the Baya Weaver bird's nest found on the Indian subcontinent and in Southeast Asia. The thermal insulation is approximately ten times better than a typical clay brick. An alternative application would be for the material to be used as large insulation panels. It is currently being trialled for constructing a model house in Saudi Arabia.

Automated Brick-Laying

State-of-the-art automated brick-laying robotics[21] can eliminate the traditional labour-intensive brick and block laying processes. The system, typically used in house building, requires the machine's frame with a robot track to be placed around the perimeter of the building. A gripper arm grabs and places the brick or block in conjunction with a nozzle which supplies the correct quantity of mortar. The placement of the masonry is pre-determined from a digitised version of the architect's drawing and high productivity is achieved compared to manual brick-laying. Quality control is assured by a professional tradesman following on the track immediately after the brick or block placement. As no manual brick-laying is necessary, scaffolding can be eliminated. The basic structure of a two-storey house can be completed in two or three weeks by an Automated Brick-laying Robot (ABLR). The system requires a labourer to load the machine with bricks and mortar. The professional tradesman inserts any necessary damp-proof courses, wall ties and lintels.

Brick Slip Cladding

Insulated brick slip panels consisting of brick slips bonded to expanded polystyrene insulation (Figure 10.12) offer a speedy retrofit where increased insulation to external walls is required to reduce heat losses. Units are manufactured to standard panel sizes which bond into special preformed quoin units. The fixed panels can then be pointed up to give the appearance of standard brickwork.

An alternative system based on stainless steel fixing rails ensures that the brick slips are mechanically retained (Figure 10.13). Frost-resistant 65mm brick slips are used and the system has an A1 fire classification to BS EN 13501-1[22] permitting its use in

Figure 10.12 Haacke® insulated brick slip cladding panel system. Photograph: Arthur Lyons

Figure 10.13 Forterra® brick cladding system using mechanically retained bricks slips on a stainless steel support system. Photograph: Arthur Lyons

buildings to any height. Various decorative patterns can be incorporated including three-dimensional effects. The brick slips are specially profiled so that they clip into the metal rails. Special corner units are available to match, and with the thicker brick slips, any standard mortar joint profile can be applied. Special shapes such as plinths can also be incorporated to enhance design features.

Wildlife Bricks and Tiles

A range of bricks and tiles have been developed to enhance biodiversity within the built environment.[23] The brick units with access holes of appropriate size are available for bats, birds, solitary bees, bumble bees and bugs. The larger units are constructed as a concrete box of the necessary size either with a cast stone or a brick slip finish to match standard 215 × 65 × 102.5mm brickwork. Units are normally incorporated into the outer leaf of cavity construction.

Standard bat boxes are as follows: 440mm or 215mm wide × 440mm high × 102mm deep and 290mm or 215mm high × 215mm wide × 102mm deep (Figure 10.14). Bat boxes should be located where they will

Figure 10.14 Bat box. Photograph: Courtesy of Ibstock Group

receive the maximum amount of sunlight from a southerly aspect. They should be 5–7 metres above ground, preferably near eaves or a gable apex, but clear of climbing plants and wall openings.

Sparrow boxes are 280 × 203 × 140mm giving internal dimensions of 230 × 153 × 140mm, with a 32mm diameter aperture. The starling box has the same dimensions but a 48mm diameter aperture (Figure 10.15).

Figure 10.15 Sparrow and starling boxes. Photograph: Courtesy of Ibstock Group

The front plate of sparrow and starling boxes can be removed for nest cleaning. Swift boxes are typically 326 × 140 × 140mm.

Bat and bird access roof tiles are manufactured to integrate into a range of plain and profile standard ceramic and concrete tiles.

The British Standard BS 8683: 2021[24] highlights the requirement to incorporate quantifiable Biodiversity Net Gain (BNG) within building developments. The standard can be related to all sizes of projects and all development sectors.

Straw Bale Construction

Straw bale construction using standard units (typically 500 × 375 × 990mm) is now well established as an ecologically friendly building system. Bales for construction purposes must be well compressed with a minimum density between 110 and 150kg/m^3 and tied with non-degrading twine such as polypropylene. They must dry to prevent the growth of moulds and fungi. For load-bearing construction the bales are stacked, large faces down in stretcher bond, making the orientation of the fibres predominantly horizontal. Lightly loaded structural walls up to two storeys high are possible. Cut bales are required for openings and at ground level straw bales must be protected from rising damp and the risk of surface water. Bales must be tightly packed to ensure stability and to reduce settling under load. Metal spikes or hazel rods at 450mm centres secure the bales which may require insecticide spray for protection. Externally a 35mm lime/clay or lime render supported on wire mesh is required. Alternatively, a rainscreen separated from the external face of the straw bales may be used. Roofs are set on a timber wall plate fixed to the top bales for stability. Internally the straw bales will require trimming prior to application of a vapour-permeable finish. Typically lime render is used. The first coat is sprayed or firmly thrown to ensure a good bond with the straw. A second and final skim coat are usually applied. The fire resistance of straw bales is similar to that of timber. Straw is also used as an insulating infill to timber frame construction as described in Chapter 18 – Insulation Materials page 197.

Straw Panel Construction

Prefabricated straw panel construction enables fast erection on site. Panels consisting of double timber frames are manufactured off-site to close tolerances to ensure easy construction on site (Figure 10.16). All architectural forms including multi-storey construction and curved walls are feasible as the units are individually manufactured and labelled for installation on site. Panels are load-bearing and require no additional structure to support floors and roofs. A base plate is required on the concrete foundations and a ring beam supports the roof structure. External finishes include an airtight membrane secured with plywood strips and wood fibreboard followed by plaster or cladding systems. Internal finishes range from clay plasters to exposed decorative timber. Rendered panels have 120 minutes' fire resistance. Construction with an interior clay plaster finish, 400mm timber/straw panel and 100mm exterior wood fibreboard has U-value of 0.119W/m^{2}K. Standard straw bale construction is described in the BRE Information Paper.[25]

Figure 10.16 Prefabricated unit of timber-secured straw for building construction. Photograph: Arthur Lyons

References

1. British Standard BS EN 771-1: 2011 + A1: 2015. *Specification for masonry units. Clay masonry units*, BSI, London.
2. *Brick firm ramps up solar power at factories to combat escalating energy costs*. Rogers, D., 6 September 2022, Building Magazine, London.
3. Brick Development Association Sustainability Report – 2022 (www. brick.org.uk).
4. *Marshalls reveals carbon reduction innovations* (whttps://www.theconstructionindex.co.uk/news/view/marshalls-reveals-carbon-reduction-innovations), 5 May 2023, The Construction Index, March, Cambridgeshire.
5. *Brick that decimates embodied carbon set to start production*, Cousins, S., 16 April 2021, RIBA Journal, London.
6. *Greenleaf Bricks* (https://www. greenleaf.com/sustainability), North Carolina, USA.
7. *Biomason Bricks* (https://biomason. com/contact), Durham, North Carolina, USA.
8. *Bio-cement from algae*, Edwards, P., 3 October 2022, Global Cement Magazine. Pro Global Media Ltd., Epsom.
9. 'Wool bricks', Hatherway, C., 17 November 2018, Wool Alliance for Social Agency, Netherlands.
10. *Powerhouses: Nanotechnology turns bricks into batteries*, Carrington, D., 11 August 2020, The Guardian, London.
11. *Unfired clay masonry – An introduction to low impact building materials*, Sutton, A., Black, D. and Walker, P., BRE IP 16/11, IHS BRE Press, Bracknell.
12. *Ibstock Ecoterre unfired clay block*, (https://www.greenspec.co.uk/green-products/unfired-clay-bricks/details/ibstock-ecoterre-brick.php/), Greenspec Ltd., Beverley.
13. *Sargablock*, (https://fortommow.org/explore-solutions/sargablock), Mkrtichian, E., 13 February 2020.
14. *The CobBauge project*, The University of Plymouth, (https://www.plymouth. ac.uk/news/construction-begins-on-innovative-cobbauge-research-building), 11 October 2021.

15. *Carbon Neutral Protocol 2023* – The global standard for carbon neutral programmes. (https://carbonneutral.com).

16. British Standard BS EN 771-3: 2011 + A1: 2015. *Specification for masonry units. Aggregate concrete masonry units (Dense and lightweight aggregates)*, BSI, London.

17. *Isotex Cement-Wood Blocks and Floor Slabs*, (https://en.blocchiisotex.com/our-range-of-blocks/), Isotex srl, Italy.

18. *Durisol Woodcrete ICF Blocks* (https://www.durisol.uk), Crumlin, Gwent.

19. *Solving the global plastic waste crisis*, ByBlock, By Fusion Global Inc., Los Angeles.

20. *De Montfort University showcases 3D printed brick made from domestic upcycled plastic waste*, Business Transformation, 2 February 2022, Monmouth, New Jersey.

21. *The automated brick-laying robot is a state-of-the-art system that automates the building of brick, block and mortar houses* (https://constructionautomation.co.uk/ablr), Construction Automation Ltd., New York.

22. British Standard BS EN 13501-1: 2018. *Fire classification of construction products and building elements – Classification using data from reaction to fire tests*, BSI, London.

23. *Ibstock habitats building in biodiversity* (https://www.ibstockbrick.co.uk/wp-content/uploads/2022/02/37069-Ibstock-EcoHabitats-eBook-v12-Download.pdf), Ibstock, Leicestershire.

24. British Standard BS 8683: 2021. *Process for designing and implementing biodiversity net gain. Specification*, BSI, London.

25. *Straw bale – An introduction to low impact building materials*, Sutton, A., Black, D. and Walker, P., BRE IP 15/11, IHS BRE Press, Bracknell.

CHAPTER 11

Cement, Concrete and Clay

CONTENTS

DOI: 10.1201/9781003360469-11

Introduction

The cement and concrete industry is conscious that it contributes a significant proportion of the world's emitted carbon dioxide and has been acting to ameliorate the situation by utilising a range of strategies.[1] These include the use of alternative fuels, the manufacture of lower-carbon cements and operating carbon capture technologies, as the emission of carbon dioxide in the manufacture of ordinary Portland cement (OPC) from limestone cannot be significantly altered. The various options are described in this chapter.

The chapter also describes other cementitious materials based on magnesium oxide, hemp and Ferrock®[2] as alternatives to the conventional calcium-based products. Furthermore, the development of carbon capture cement offers a realistic opportunity for permanently sequestering the CO_2 necessarily evolved in cement manufacture and even captured from other industrial processes, although clearly this technology is easier to accomplish within a factory environment rather than on-site.

Alternative reinforcement materials are considered although many are only experimental. The development of 3D-printing is rapidly advancing and will no doubt have a major contribution to construction methods in the near future.

Various specialist products including self-healing, photoluminescent, light-transmitting concrete and electrical storage are described, although some are still at the development stage. Cob and rammed earth remain specialist alternatives to cement-based construction materials.

Portland Cement

Portland is the principal form of cement manufactured globally, and during its production from calcium carbonate, it necessarily releases carbon dioxide by the decomposition of limestone (calcium carbonate) into lime (calcium oxide). Approximately 62% of the CO_2 emissions are from calcination and 35% associated with the energy required to fire the kilns to 1450°C. Approximately 8% of world and 1.5% of UK carbon dioxide emissions are associated with the production of cement as it is such a widely used commodity. The UK industry is making strenuous efforts to achieve a 55% reduction in CO_2 emissions by 2030, which equates roughly to a target of $550 kgCO_2$ per tonne and net zero by 2050.

One cement plant at Rugby intends to eliminate the use of fossil fuels by operating 100% on Climafuel®[3], a waste-derived fuel from a mixture of household and commercial residues which otherwise go to landfill sites. Over the calendar year, the

Rugby plant is expected to achieve a 70% alternative fuel substitution. Broadly, Cemex[®4] anticipated a 40% reduction in its carbon emissions within Europe by the end of 2022. Other carbon-reducing fuels such as hydrogen and plasma are currently being researched alongside carbon capture and storage including the use of algae. Hanson[®5] is currently researching the use of hydrogen as a fuel at its cement and asphalt factories around the UK, through the 'Industrial Hydrogen Accelerator' programme funded by the UK Department for Business, Energy and Industrial Strategy (BEIS). However, the supply of hydrogen may be limited because of the demands of other key industries – particularly steel.

The typical embodied carbon content in Ordinary Portland Cement (OPC) is 0.91kgCO$_2$e/kg, although the UK average is 0.86kgCO$_2$e/kg. The aim of the cement industry is to significantly reduce the carbon footprint of cement by a combination of switching fuels, the use of more energy-efficient transport and modifications to the input feed. Certainly long-term the current development of carbon capture and storage (CCS) will help to alleviate this problem.

Alternative Low-Carbon Cements

Currently, the well-established method for reducing the embodied carbon of cement for use in concrete involves the use of Supplementary Cementitious Materials (SCMs) such as fly ash and GGBS. Fly ash is the residue from generating electricity from coal, and ground granulated blast-furnace slag (GGBS) is produced in the manufacture of steel. Both of these materials may well decline in availability as less electricity is generated from coal-fired stations and more steel is recycled from demolition sites and general waste. However, in the interim, these SCMs offer a good method for reducing CO$_2$ emissions. CEMV/B with 36% GGBS has an embodied carbon content of 0.284kgCO$_2$e/kg, while CEM III/C with 88% GGBS has an embodied carbon content of 0.147kgCO$_2$e/kg.

The standard BS EN 197-5: 2021[6] (Table I) and the new British Standard BS 8500: 2023[7] incorporate cements with lower embodied carbon and regularise the use of low-carbon multicomponent cements based on the incorporation of limestone.

CEM II/ C-M permits cement clinker content in the range of 50–64% blended up to 50% other SCMs.

CEM VI/ S-LL permits a minimum of 35% cement clinker with a maximum of 59% GGBS and 20% limestone.

Supplementary Cementitious Materials (SCMs)

Cementitious materials are predominantly based on calcium, silicon and aluminium oxides. Unlike calcium which naturally occurs as calcium carbonate, natural sources of silicon and aluminium are not present as carbonates and therefore do not evolve CO$_2$ when calcined for cement. Common alternative SCMs include calcined clays, silica fume, burnt shale, natural pozzolana and rice husk ash. Naturally abundant kaolinite clay, rich in silica and alumina, can be calcined at 700–850°C to form an alternative SCM. An additional

SCM is ground uncalcined limestone which can be added to Portland cements in modest quantities. The standard compositions are listed in Table 11.1.

In the short term, it is anticipated that CEM II/A-LL with only 80–94% cement clinker and 6–20% limestone will replace the current standard CEM I with 95–100% cement clinker. So, Portland/limestone cement will become the standard material rather than Portland cement. Even this action will immediately reduce carbon emissions from the cement factories.

In the slightly longer term, the ternary (three component) cements will become more common with typical compositions:

CEM II/C-M Fly ash ternary cement: 50% clinker, 10–40% fly ash, 10–15% limestone.

CEM VI (S-LL) GGBS ternary cement: 35% clinker, 30–55% GGBS, 10–15% limestone.

Ultimately, as shortages of GGBS and fly ash materialise these constituents will be replaced with natural pozzolana (P) and calcined clays (Q). The use of rice husk ash with durian pectin as a partial replacement for cement is currently under research in Malaysia.

Currently, 140 billion tonnes of biomass is generated from world agriculture every year. The residue arising from straw, stalks, leaves, seed husks, wood and farmyards is frequently burnt as fuel. If fired at 600–700°C, the residual ashes, which are largely considered a waste product, have the potential to be used as Supplementary Cementitious

Table 11.1 Portland-composite cement and composite cement to BS EN 197–5: 2021

Type	Name	Notation	Clinker	Blast-furnace slag	Other constituents	Minor additional constituents
CEM II	Portland composite cement	CEM II/C-M	50–64	36–50 (S D^b P Q V W T L^c LL^c)		0.5
CEM VI	Composite cement	CEM VI (S-P)	35–49	31–59	Natural pozzolana 6–20	0.5
		CEM VI (S-V)	35–49	31–59	Siliceaous fly ash 6–20	0.5
		CEM VI (S-L)	35–49	31–59	Limestone L^c 6–20	0.5
		CEM VI (S-LL)	35–49	31–59	Limestone LL^c 6–20	0.5

Notes: Percentages by mass.
K-Clinker, S-Blast-furnace slag, D^b Silica fume, P-Natural pozzolana, Q-Natural calcined pozzolana, V-Siliceous fly ash, W-calcareous fly ash, T-Burnt shale, L^c-Limestone, LL^c-Limestone.

Materials (SCMs).[8] Potentially approximately 3.7 billion tonnes of this material is currently available. The most promising materials derive from rice husks,[9] sugar bagasse and wheat straw.

As concrete is generally a local product the types and quantities of supplementary cementitious materials incorporated will vary significantly across the world.

Limestone Calcined Clay Cement (LC3)

The recent development of limestone calcined clay cement (LC3), with a typical composition of 50% clinker, 30% calcined kaolinite clay, 15% limestone and 5% gypsum offers a 30% reduction in CO_2 emissions. This material produces a cement with mechanical properties comparable to CEM I at seven days. However, the supply of high-grade kaolin clay is rather limited in the UK compared to elsewhere in Europe, Asia and the Americas. Clays have the advantage that they are calcined at 800°C rather than the 1450°C which is required to produce Portland cement clinker.

Alkali-Activated Materials/ Geopolymers

In the long term, alternative cementitious materials may totally replace Portland cement clinker. Geopolymers are defined as minerals broadly based on sodium or potassium aluminosilicates rather than calcium silicates and aluminates as in Portland cement. Earth Friendly Concrete[10] (EFC®)/Geopolymer Concrete is usually manufactured from GGBS and fly ash. It is activated with an alkali such as sodium hydroxide and contains no Portland cement. The product is durable and resistant to chloride and sulphate salts. It offers a significant saving of embodied energy and typically a reduction of 64% CO_{2e} compared to standard Portland cement concrete. It also has high early strength, greater durability and good fire and chloride resistance. Alternative minerals high in alumina and silica include volcanic rocks, lateritic soils and kaolin clays. They can be heated and crushed to form cementitious materials. Alternative activators (PAS 8820: 2016[11]) include sodium silicate, potassium silicate, sodium carbonate and sodium sulphate. The activators are required to raise the pH of the mix sufficiently to induce the solidification process.

The low-carbon Vertua®[12] geopolymer clinker-free cement, with a 70% reduction in CO_2 compared to CEM1, uses carbon offsetting to obtain an overall carbon-neutral concrete. Carbon credits are purchased in accordance with the Carbon Neutral Protocol.[13]

Cemfree®[14] uses 95% ground granulated blast-furnace slag (GGBFS) and 5% alkali activator giving CO_2 emissions of 114 kg/t which corresponds to a 77% reduction compared to standard ordinary Portland cement (OPC).

However, where the use of novel cements is anticipated, the material has to be sufficiently verified by appropriate testing including stress deflection and exposure if it is not covered by existing standards in the relevant country. Niche cements such as calcium aluminate cement, calcium sulphoaluminate cement and calcium metasilicate cement are not currently included within the British Standard BS 8500: 2023[7].

Magnesium Oxide Cement

Cements derived from magnesium silicate and magnesium carbonate (Eco-Cement®[15]) are currently under development. Magnesium silicate has the advantage that when heated in a kiln to between 600°C and 750°C during its conversion to magnesium oxide cement no CO_2 is evolved. The energy used in manufacturing 1 tonne of this material produces 0.4 tonnes of CO_2, but it subsequently absorbs 1.1 tonnes during the recarbonation process, leaving a reduction of 0.7 tonnes from the atmosphere. The recarbonation process is inhibited if the product is not permeable, so quantities of fine additions to the mix must be limited. However, more waste materials can be incorporated as it is less alkaline than standard Portland cement, thus reducing the risk of delayed detrimental reactions. In the long term, magnesium oxide cement is unlikely to totally replace standard Portland cement, as the worldwide supplies of magnesium carbonate and magnesium silicate are limited compared to those of calcium carbonate, especially within the UK. However, a current estimate by Novacem® puts the global reserves of magnesium silicates as being in excess of 10,000 billion tonnes.

Research at Sheffield Hallam University[16] produced Liquid Granite® from >60% crystalline silica sand and 10–35% magnesium oxide, of which 30–70% is industrial waste. The material uses the same aggregates as normal concrete and replaces two-thirds of the Portland cement normally used in concrete production. The concrete produced is fire-resistant to 1100°C and will not explode when exposed to fire. A rapid-setting version as a repair mortar incorporates a polymer-modified liquid admixture.

An alternative approach is to replace just 35% of the Portland cement in a standard mix with processed magnesium silicate (olivine). The processing of olivine produces silica and magnesium oxide but no CO_2 as unlike calcium carbonate, there is no carbon in the base material. The magnesium component becomes carbonated to form magnesium carbonate by taking in carbon dioxide making the overall process carbon neutral.

Carbon-Neutral Cement

A variation in the processing of olivine (magnesium silicate) is currently under development at Imperial College London.[17] The process involves combining crushed olivine with by-product carbon dioxide from industrial flue gases to produce silica, which can then be used as a supplementary cementitious material (SCM) in concrete mixes. The by-product of the Seratech®[18] process is magnesium carbonate which permanently sequesters the carbon dioxide. The replacement of 35% of the Portland cement in a standard mix with the silica produced in this process makes concrete production virtually carbon neutral. The magnesium carbonate produced as a by-product can be used to produce other carbon-neutral construction materials such as building blocks and plasterboard.

Recycled Concrete Cement

Cambridge University[19] is investigating the possibility of producing cement from recycled concrete. In order to make the slag required in the electric arc furnace (EAF) method for making steel, lime is mixed with the recycled scrap steel. The slag produced is not cementitious and of no real value. However, if the lime is replaced by concrete waste – recovered cement paste (RCP), then the slag produced is similar to standard Portland cement clinker. The usual addition of gypsum converts it into Portland cement. The process is still under development, but if successful it will be scaled up to large-scale testing in a commercial electric arc furnace.

Biochar Admixture

Current research[20] is investigating the effect of adding biochar into cement. Biochar is produced by the pyrolysis of waste wood products in the absence of oxygen. (Described in more detail in Chapter 18 – Insulation Materials page 202). The pyrolysis of wood, chipboard, plywood and MDF drives off much of the impurities such as glue, paint or resin leaving a reasonably pure charcoal. This product is ground down to a fine powder with a particle size of about 50 microns. If used as a 1 or 2% cement substitute in a concrete mix, the charcoal acts as a micro-sponge absorbing moisture and accelerating the initial curing process, which could speed up precast production. The stored water is then available for the subsequent stages of the curing process, making potentially a more compact and therefore waterproof concrete.

Carbon-Capturing Cement

Carbon dioxide from the atmosphere is slowly absorbed into concrete turning the calcium hydroxide into calcium carbonate. The natural carbonation process takes place over a period of years and only approximately one-third of the CO_2 produced in concrete manufacture is ultimately reabsorbed.

A significant proportion of carbon capture cement is based on GGBS from the steel industry, rather than lime-based Portland cement, so there is little or no requirement to burn off carbon dioxide from natural limestone to produce calcium oxide. This reduces the heating energy and emissions involved compared to ordinary Portland cement production. The common curing process involves pressure impregnation of the cast units with carbon dioxide which converts the calcium oxide into calcium carbonate. The process is only applicable to factory-produced blocks and precast units where pressurised CO_2 can be applied. The resulting carbonated concrete has a 30% enhanced compressive strength compared to conventional concrete and the hardening process takes only 24 hours compared to several days of standard curing. The carbon dioxide used can be taken from other industrial processes which incorporate carbon capture to prevent the CO_2 from escaping into the atmosphere. The process can only replace 20% of world Portland cement production due to limitations on supply of slag from steel production. However, the combination of carbon capture, utilisation and storage can deliver approximately 60% of the carbon reductions necessary for the UK cement and concrete industry to be carbon neutral by 2050.

Solidia®[21] cement developed in the USA, is based on low-lime calcium silicates (wollastonite and rankinite) which are chamber-cured by carbon dioxide and moisture to produce calcite ($CaCO_3$) and silica (SiO_2). Standard Portland cement contains over 70% lime, whereas the lime content of Solidia® is around 48%. The material is manufactured using the same technology as Portland cement but the reduced lime content permits the sintering process to occur at the lower temperature of 1200°C, compared to 1450°C for Portland cement. This significantly reduces the fuel consumption and the corresponding CO_2 emissions which are approximately 190 kg per tonne. The calcining of Solidia cement to clinker produces $375kgCO_2$ per tonne. Overall production of Solidia® cement is accomplished with about a 30% reduction of CO_2 emissions compared to Portland cement and also less water consumption.

An alternative process by CarbonBuilt®[22] incorporates hydrated lime to the concrete mix as this increases the rate of carbon dioxide absorption during curing within a carbon dioxide chamber. This significantly reduces the carbon footprint of concrete block production.

In the North American process, CarbonCure®,[23] previously captured carbon dioxide is introduced into the concrete mix in the form of 'dry ice' crystals to react quickly with the calcium oxide forming calcium carbonate. Currently, carbon dioxide, as the waste product from other industrial processes such as the manufacture of fertiliser, is used, although there is the potential to capture the gas from cement manufacture or extract it directly from the air. The CO_2 is injected into the mix as dry ice to prevent loss during batching and is added at the rate of approximately 0.2%, so has no effect on slump, temperature or the ultimate pH of the mix. The process increases the 7-day strength of a standard mix concrete by 8% and by 7% after 28 days. Alternatively, incorporating CO_2 can reduce the cement content necessary for standard strength requirements. No voids are left in the hardened concrete. However, the process takes back only about 5% of the CO_2 produced in the production of the concrete mix. The system can be used for precast or ready-mix applications.

Programmable Cement

Researchers at Rice University, Texas,[24] have shown that by adding negatively and positively charged surfactants to a cement mix, the form into which the cement particles set can be controlled. Normally cement sets into a disordered array of microscopic particles, but under the influence of specific surfactants, the semi-crystalline forms are well-ordered shapes including cubes which pack together more closely. The concrete produced is therefore denser, more durable and less porous. The reduced porosity reduces the ingress of moisture and chemicals which can lead to the corrosion of steel reinforcements. Overall the incorporation of these surfactants can potentially reduce the quantity of concrete required for construction projects giving significant environmental gain.

Ferrock

Ferrock[2] is a cement substitute formed from 95% recycled materials. The standard composition is waste steel dust and silica from recycled glass, with the addition of virgin iron-rich rock. When mixed with water the material sets to a solid which is significantly stronger than the standard Portland cement concrete (34.5–48 MPa). Ferrock is also more flexible than conventional concrete making it appropriate for use in seismic locations. During solidification, the iron component absorbs carbon dioxide to produce iron carbonate making Ferrock an environmentally friendly cement substitute. Ferrock is durable, resistant to UV and chemical attack and can be used in marine environments. However, the material is only suitable for relatively small projects due to the restricted availability of steel dust which is the key constituent.

Future Cement Industry Developments

Currently, a small proportion of waste industrial carbon dioxide is being removed from the atmosphere by Carbon Capture and Storage (CCS). However, a wide range of systems for carbon capture are currently under investigation or development. At this stage, it is difficult to predict which ones will ultimately be commercially viable.

One cement plant in Heidelberg[25] will capture 100,000 tonnes of CO_2 a year which will be compressed and permanently stored in an empty oil reservoir under the North Sea. Alternative storage is within geological formations under the sea or in voids left after natural gas extraction. The storage has to be at least 1 km below the rock surface to be effective.

Hanson®[26] is developing a carbon capture plant at Padeswood in Fintshire which, when it opens in 2024, will capture approximately 800,000 tonnes of CO_2 annually. The process involves absorbing the flue gasses in an organic amine solvent at 40°C inside an 80m-high absorber. The CO_2 enriched amine is then heated to 120°C to release the carbon dioxide. The amine is recycled and the CO_2 is compressed and will be piped 10 km into the local area network (HyNet[27]) which then takes the gas into permanent storage in the seabed of Liverpool Bay in the Irish Sea. The process of capturing CO_2 is however energy intensive using approximately the same amount of energy to capture 1 tonne of carbon dioxide as it takes to produce 1 tonne of cement.

One form of carbon capture currently under investigation by HeidelbergCement®[28] is the use of algae to absorb CO_2.[10] An array of plastic tubes is filled with a mixture of algae and seawater. When the algae have grown to twice their own weight by absorbing CO_2, they are removed from the brine and dried in sun-heated air, producing algae flakes which can be used as fish food or chicken feed. Currently, at the Heidelberg-Cement factory in Morocco the algae system covering just one hectare removes a very small proportion of the carbon dioxide output, but scaling up to 400 ha is anticipated when 10% of the factory CO_2 output would be absorbed.

HeidelbergCement is also developing an industrial-scale plant in Brevik,[29] Norway, to recarbonate recycled concrete using the flue gases from the standard Portland cement kiln. Crushed concrete waste is separated into cement hydrates, aggregate and sand. The lime-based component is contained as a semi-dry fluidised bed through which carbon dioxide flue gases are passed. The enforced carbonation produces calcite, which in the presence of the silica and alumina in the original clinker, produces a pozzolanic material which can then be used as a supplementary cementitious material (SCM) in new concrete production.

Other carbon capture techniques under consideration include the use of solid-state metal-organic frameworks which specifically absorb carbon dioxide from flue gasses under pressure followed by a vacuum cycle to release and capture the carbon dioxide thus regenerating the absorbent material. The MOF Technologies®[30] process uses 80% less energy than carbon capture by the use of amine solvent systems.

Longer-term ideas include the mass production of cement using hydrogen fuel. Currently, one Hanson UK cement kiln has demonstrated that it can be operated successfully using a mix of hydrogen with glycerine and biomass by-products from other industries.[31] The climate-neutral mix of fuels contained 39% grey hydrogen, 12% meat and bone meal (MBM) and 49% glycerine.

One option being researched is the use of local wind and solar to produce electricity which would then be directly used for water electrolysis into hydrogen and oxygen to be used as the fuel system in the calcining plant. Battery storage would be necessary to ensure continuity of the process and waste heat recovery would also reduce energy requirements. Carbon sequestering by the planting of trees would give added support to the overall system.

Concrete Reinforcement Materials

Steel for reinforcement typically accounts for 19% of the carbon emissions associated within reinforced concrete. Responsibly sourced steel reinforcement schemes are ECO-Reinforcement to BES 6001[32] and CARES Sustainable Construction Steels (SCS) scheme to BS 8902: 2009.[33]

Basalt[34] in the form of chopped strand, mesh and composite rebars (Figure 11.1) offers an alternative to steel reinforcement. The composite bars are manufactured by pultrusion from a mixture of basalt fibre and resin. The material has high-tensile strength and good corrosion resistance.

Hemp rebar[35] is manufactured from a combination of the fibre from hemp stalks and thermoplastic resin. The hemp rebar is made by a pultrusion process. The fibres are pulled through a heated die with thermoplastic resin to form a rope which is then heat-treated and cut to form solid bars. It is anticipated that bioplastics will be used in future to reduce the carbon footprint of the product. It is hoped that the development of hemp rebar will produce a material as strong as steel reinforcement, but with the

Figure 11.1 Bastech® – Basalt FRP rebar decarbonising concrete reinforced structures. Photograph: Courtesy of Basalt Technologies UK Ltd.

advantage that it is corrosion resistant and with a lower-carbon footprint.

Current researchers at the University of Bath, UK, and the University of Pittsburgh, USA, are investigating the use of titanium bars for concrete reinforcement.[36] The stress-strain behaviour of titanium is similar to that of steel, although it is half as stiff and twice as strong as the steel normally used for reinforcement.

The Technical University of Dresden is investigating the potential for replacing steel reinforcement with carbon-fibre yarn.[37] Ultra-thin carbon fibres are bound together to form a yarn which is then formed into a mesh. The resulting concrete is four times stronger than standard concrete and also four times lighter due to the reduction in size of necessary sections. As carbon-fibre mesh is rust-proof the required cover, to prevent corrosion in conventional reinforced concrete, can be reduced. This in turn reduces the carbon footprint of the reinforced concrete project by up to 50%, by using considerably less material. However, the carbon footprint of carbon fibre as currently produced is high, so research is progressing to create bio-based carbon fibres from plant-based lignin.

Bamboo, as a cheap and available material, has been suggested as an alternative reinforcement to steel. However, it does have high water absorption and low bonding strength to concrete. This can be overcome by the incorporation of waterproofing agent in the mix. Flexural testing and pull-out testing on bamboo reinforced beams suggest that bamboo might be useable as an alternative material in reinforced concrete,[38] but other published research[39] suggested strongly that bamboo reinforced concrete is not a viable material.

Graphene and Alternative Fibres

Fibre reinforcement offers a reduced carbon footprint compared to traditional steel or stainless steel mesh reinforcement.

Polypropylene monofilament fibres[40] (Figure 11.2) and macrofibres (Figure 11.3) offer a 61% reduction in CO_2 compared to traditional A142 high-tensile steel mesh; similarly, hook-end steel fibres (Figure 11.4) offer an equivalent 54% reduction in CO_2.

Hemp and recycled aggregates concrete (HRAC) using 20–30 mm hemp fibres offers a more sustainable material than traditional fibre-reinforced concrete. The hemp fibres are pre-treated with alkali or acetyl to increase crystallinity. The material has a lower compressive strength and modulus of elasticity than standard concrete but flexural strength is unaffected.

Alternative fibres under investigation include bamboo, also current research is investigating the addition of vegetable particles such as sugar beet which can strengthen concrete while reducing the volume of cement required.

The discovery of graphene forms the basis of a major innovation for the cement and concrete industry. Graphene is composed of a single layer of carbon atoms in the form of nano-platelets. It is 200 times stronger than steel and can be incorporated into a concrete mix as a liquid admixture which ensures thorough mixing. The graphene enhances the hydration process and microstructural development during curing. This leads to increased compressive, flexural and tensile shear strength in the cured concrete. Research has demonstrated that graphene-enhanced concrete 'Concretene'[®41] is less permeable than the equivalent standard material, therefore more durable and less vulnerable to degradation by alkali-silica reaction. The addition of about 0.01% by volume of graphene into standard RC30 concrete for light-wearing surfaces and foundations can eliminate or reduce the steel reinforcement required, give a 30% reduction in the necessary volume of concrete and reduce its cement content. In addition as 'Concretene' does not shrink,

Figure 11.2 Polypropylene fibres for concrete reinforcement. Photograph: Arthur Lyons.

movement joints can be eliminated and fire resistance is enhanced. These savings produce a significant reduction in the overall emissions of CO_2 in relation to production, transportation and placement of concrete. The normal concrete batching and placing techniques can be deployed for 'Concretene'.

Current research is investigating the use of GGBS (ground granulated blast-furnace slag), silica fume and other cementitious materials as alternatives to standard Portland cement in graphene concrete. Formal accreditation for 'Concretene' is anticipated through the relevant authorities.

Figure 11.3 Adfil Durus EasyFinish® polypropylene macro-synthetic fibres for concrete reinforcement.
Photograph: Arthur Lyons

Recycled Fibres

Recycled steel tyre microfibres[42] (RSTM), which are extracted by Zero Waste Works®, from post-consumer tyres, offer an ecological alternative to the use of new steel fibres in concrete, mortar and grout. The high-strength but flexible fibres form a dense reinforcing network in concrete and give good control over micro-cracking similar to traditional rebar or standard steel fibres. The recycled fibres have a 95% reduced carbon footprint compared to the new product.

Recycled steel undulated fibres (RSUF) are a by-product of the production of steel

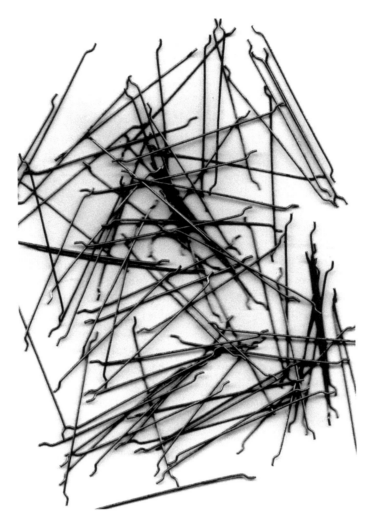

Figure 11.4 Adfil® hook-end steel fibre reinforcement for concrete. Photograph: Arthur Lyons

wool. The waste wire is post-processed into fibre reinforcement for concrete. The undulating form of the fibres and their grooved surface ensures good bonding to the concrete matrix, which reduces shrinkage cracking during the setting process. The material is appropriate for mass concrete in industrial floors, pavements, tunnel linings and precast concrete units. The fibres are 51 mm in length with a cross-section of 2.8 mm × 0.7 mm and a tensile strength of 900 MPa.

Recycled polymer tyre microfibres (RPTM) are an alternative to conventional polypropylene fibres for use within concrete to prevent spalling in the case of fire. Also recycled polypropylene fibres can be used as an alternative to new fibres to prevent plastic shrinkage during the initial drying and setting of concrete. The recycled fibres range in length from 2 mm to 6 mm with diameters within the range of 11–23ηm. The melting point of recycled polypropylene fibres ranges between 210°C and 260°C.

Ashcrete

Fly ash from the burning of coal is the main component of ashcrete which inevitably means that CO_2 is being produced. However, considerably less CO_2 is emitted in producing one tonne of fly ash compared to the manufacture of one tonne of Portland cement. Also the fly ash from burning coal is essentially a by-product from other industrial processes including generating electricity. Ashcrete contains about 93% recycled materials, made up of fly ash, borate, bottom ash and a chlorine compound. The fly ash used within ashcrete is predominantly the Class C type which has a high calcium content and less than 2% carbon.

Ashcrete has a low embodied energy compared to traditional cement and, as a by-product of other industrial processes, is cheaper than Portland cement. Ashcrete is stronger, more durable and less permeable than Portland cement concrete due to the fine particles in fly ash and their pozzolanic properties which reduce cracking after setting. The spherical shape of the fly ash particles allows for less water in the concrete mix giving greater workability and pumpability. This in turn produces a concrete with a reduced shrinkage on setting and hardening. However, ashcrete requires a longer setting time and is slower than Portland cement to reach maximum strength, which has implications on larger projects. It also cannot be used in low temperatures and does incorporate a noxious chlorine-based compound. Ashcrete is well established as a construction material in America, particularly for large dams due to its strength and resistance to water damage. Ashcrete also has good fire resistance.

Hempcrete

Hempcrete[43] is manufactured from hemp hurds (stalks), sand and lime. Hemp is a fast-growing plant which is easily grown and requires little water (Figure 11.5). It is grown predominantly for the manufacture of paper and textiles but the remaining 75% of the hemp hurds or shiv, the woody core, can be used for the manufacture of hempcrete. When mixed with hydraulic lime it produces a cement mixture which sets within a few hours and then petrifies over a few weeks to a lightweight solid due to the high silica content of hemp hurds. Hempcrete is a lightweight material ideal for in-situ self-insulating walls and screeds and also for the manufacture of insulating blocks. The material can be either cast within formwork or trowelled. Hempcrete should not be used below ground level, and any exposed material should be protected from the weather during the drying-out period. On site, dry hempcrete can be worked using standard tools as for lightweight aircrete blocks. Any finishes applied to hempcrete must be vapour permeable to prevent trapped moisture from the material. The thermal mass of

Figure 11.5 Hemp crop in Australia. Photograph: Courtesy of Mirreco®[45]

hempcrete construction together with its insulating and humidity-controlling properties assist in the stabilisation of internal environments. Hempcrete is fire and vermin proof without requiring the addition of chemical agents.

Hempcrete is an ideal material for infill within timber frame construction. The timber framework should be totally encased by the hempcrete as illustrated in Figure 11.6. The UK mix is typically three volumes of hemp shiv to one volume of lime and one volume of water, although some European countries incorporate clay which produces a denser material with less insulating properties.

Hempcrete is a carbon-negative material as the plants grow to about 4 m in four or five months absorbing more CO_2 than is emitted in their conversion to hempcrete on site. The hemp plant is naturally pest-resistant, so no chemical fertilisers or weed

Figure 11.6 Model timber frame construction with hemp blockwork to the exterior. Infill and the internal surface made with hempcrete mix. Photograph: Arthur Lyons

killers are required in its agricultural production. At the end-of-life, the material can be either remixed with new material or used as biomass. If deposited in landfill, hempcrete slowly releases its carbon content by decomposition.

Hempcrete has been used as the major construction material for several housing developments in Australia as illustrated by Figure 11.7. Mirreco® anticipate the production of 2.4 × 1.2 m hemp cast boards in the near future.[44]

Timbercrete

Timbercrete[46] (also known as woodcrete) is made from a mixture of wood chips and cement. It has the advantage over traditional concrete in that it incorporates recycled wood waste and makes a lighter material that reduces transportation emissions. It can be used as a direct replacement for normal concrete or the production of standard blocks and insulated concrete form (ICF) units, as described in Chapter 10 – Masonry

Figure 11.7 Hempcrete housing, Denmark, West Australia. Photograph: Arthur Lyons

and Alternative Units page 78. Timbercrete is fire-resistant, moisture and rot resistant and contains no VOCs.

Sugarcrete

The University of East London, in partnership with Grimshaw Architects and Tate & Lyle Sugar, has developed a new material called Sugarcrete.[47] The material is formed from a mixture of bagasse and mineral binders. Bagasse is the plant waste after sugar cane has been crushed to extract the sugar juice. It is therefore a waste by-product of the sugar industry. Sugar cane is fast growing, quickly converting CO_2 into biomass. The material,

Sugarcrete® is fire-resistant and has good insulating properties.

3D-Printed Formwork

3D-printed formwork can be used to create innovative designs in concrete structural units which can therefore be designed to optimise concrete usage when compared to flat units cast against standard formwork. Bespoke-designed formwork can create architectural features such as ribs and organic forms. The formation of voids allows for the easy integration of ducting and other services within the cast in-situ concrete. 3D-printed formwork units are usually manufactured in a lightweight concrete.

In addition to their use for in-situ concrete work, 3D-printed formwork is ideal for the production of off-site manufactured units such as stairs, façade panels and public sculpture.

Bendable Concrete

Bendable concrete[48] also known as Engineered Cementitious Composites (ECC) is a class of ultra-ductile fibre-reinforced composites. The easily moulded mortar is based on fine aggregate materials together with Portland cement and other cementitious materials such as fly ash, silica fume and blast-furnace slag with approximately 2% of short fibres. A range of fibres may be used including coir, jute or slip-coated polymers. Coated polymer fibres allow slippage rather than fracture when overloaded. A typical material is 50 times more flexible than traditional concrete and therefore has applications in seismic zones.

Permeable Concrete

Fast-draining flood-reducing concrete is for use in SuDS (Sustainable Drainage Systems), such as streets, pavements, driveways and parking areas. Typical void contents range from 15 to 35% allowing surface water to drain into the sub-strata and dissipate naturally. It is manufactured from cement, coarse aggregate and water with little or no sand, creating the porous structure.

A new alternative[49] involves the use of self-compacting cementitious material poured around a permanent formwork of vertical tubes manufactured from recycled plastic. The spacing and diameter of the formwork tubes, typically 6 mm in diameter, can be adjusted to particular requirements. For heavily loaded areas wider spacing of the tubes and the use of a large aggregate mix may be appropriate. Steel reinforcement may also be incorporated, which is not possible in open-structure permeable concrete due to water ingress causing corrosion.

Self-Healing Concrete

Self-healing concrete[50] manufactured by Sensicrete®[51] and Basilisk®[52] contains specialist bacteria which in the presence of moisture produce limestone. The bacteria can lie dormant in capsules containing food – calcium lactate – within the concrete matrix for many years, but are activated when moisture seeps into the concrete cracks and dissolves the capsules. The bacteria then feed on the lactate, multiply and produce limestone. Once the crack is sealed and no further water seeps into the concrete, the bacteria become dormant again and are only reactivated if further water enters the concrete. The bacteria can live for up to 200 years without water or oxygen, so the process can cover the normal lifetime of the concrete. The bacteria (*Bacillus pseudofirmus and Sporosarcina pasteurii*) can either be applied as a spray or included in the original concrete or mortar mix. Only small cracks, up to 0.8 mm in width can be self-healed by this process, but it has potential to significantly reduce building maintenance costs.

The material is particularly appropriate for use where the concrete becomes inaccessible in use, such as in bridges, tunnels and coastal structures. The bacteria will function in a low-carbon concrete mix incorporating ggbs (ground granulated blast-furnace slag) and/or pfa (pulverised fuel ash) – typically 71% Portland cement rather than 87%. The self-healing effect can extend the useful life of the concrete by 30% as it is reactivated when further moisture-filled cracks develop over time. Typically cracks are fully healed within 28 days, thus protecting any steel reinforcement from corrosion and the concrete returns to 90% of its original strength. A repairs compound is commercially available.

Biomineralized Concrete

A similar technology for that used in self-healing concrete can be used to create concrete bricks. A mixture of sand, calcium chloride, gelatine and growth enzymes is poured into brick-shaped moulds and photosynthetic bacteria are added.[53] The cyanobacteria absorb light in a photosynthesis mechanism and grow consuming the nutrients and moisture. The gel sets and the bacteria produce calcium carbonate making the mixture solid. The bacteria reproduce, and if more sand, gelatine and nutrients are added, further solidification of the medium takes place. The bricks produced are tough but not quite as strong as standard bricks.

Concrete Canvas

Concrete Canvas®[54] consists of a fibrous matrix which is filled with dry cementitious mix which is then hydrated on site to activate the setting and hardening process. The product is within the class of innovative materials called Geosynthetic Cementitious Composite Mats (GCCMs). Typical thicknesses of the material which is delivered to site as a roll are 5, 8 and 13 mm. Roll widths are 1.0 and 1.1 m. Standard uses include erosion and weed control, storm-water drainage and slope protection. The matrix may be backed with a waterproof PVC layer for lining. The material can be hydrated by spraying or total immersion in fresh or salt water.

Pigmented Concrete

Pigmented concrete is produced by the addition of mineral pigments during the mixing process either as powder or as liquid. The colours include yellow and red from iron oxides, chromium and cobalt produce green and blue. Black is produced from iron oxide and carbon. Titanium oxide produces a whitening effect. Some of the brighter colours such as brilliant violet and canary yellow require the use of synthetic pigments, but these are more expensive than the natural minerals. The advantage of pigmentation over surface colouration with dyes is that the all-through colour will not rub off or fade with heat or UV light. The minerals are added to the mix usually at the rate of 1 to 6% depending on the strength of colour required. The concrete produced normally has a slightly lower strength than the equivalent unpigmented product.

Electrically Conductive Concrete

Electrically conductive concrete[55] incorporating steel/stainless steel/carbon fibres or carbon/graphite powder has uses in infrastructure applications such as cathodic protection, heated surfaces and structural health monitoring. A typical mix comprises long and short steel fibres and conducting powder within a standard concrete mix. Iron ore may be incorporated to enhance the conductivity. Passive uses, not requiring an electrical supply, include electrical grounding and electromagnetic wave shielding.

Magnetisable Concrete

A patented concrete manufactured from recycled materials and incorporating ferrite is magnetisable.[56] The material produces a magnetic field enabling the wireless recharging of electric vehicles either in static locations such as scooter stands or dynamically for forklift trucks on factory floors or electric vehicles driving along specialist road lanes.

The wireless charging has a transmission efficiency of 90–95%, and the system is robust for integration into factory floors or road surfaces. The standard system consists of precast units which are incorporated into the working surface. Energy metering and billing can be automatic and indicated on-screen within the moving vehicle.

Light-Transmitting Concrete

Optical glass fibres embedded within concrete permit light to be transmitted through the solid material[57] (Figure 11.8). The fibres must go right through the material so they are placed during the casting process. Typically 5% by weight of optical fibres produces about 2% of light transmission through the translucent concrete. The thickness of the optical fibres can vary according to the required light transmission, but is typically $250\eta m$. Ordinary Portland cement and fine sand (1.18 mm sieve) form the concrete matrix. Block or panel units can be naturally illuminated or artificially lit with single colours or special effects creating interesting floors, walls and ceilings.

Light-Reflecting Concrete

Light-reflecting concrete[58] combines the standard properties of ordinary concrete with the additional property of retro-reflection which returns the incoming light in the direction from which it came. The effect therefore varies according to the position of the light source and the location of the recipient. The surface appears to switch on and off as the observer moves in relation to the light source, which may be either sunlight or artificial. The material has potential applications, particularly for interior design.

Photoluminescent Aggregate Concrete

The incorporation of photoluminescent aggregate in concrete enables it to glow-in-the-dark[59] (Figure 11.9). To operate successfully the aggregate must be exposed to the surface to receive and store light

Figure 11.8 Litracon light-transmitting concrete. Photograph: Courtesy of Litracon, Hungary

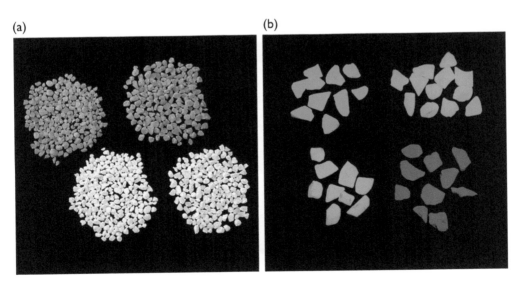

Figure 11.9 Glow stones by day (a) and by night (b). Photograph: Courtesy of AGT® Ambient Glow Technology

energy during the daytime prior to night-timeluminescence. Therefore the special aggregate is distributed into the surface of fresh concrete, sprayed with retarder then washed giving a textured surface. If a smooth surface is required the aggregate can be exposed by mechanical or hand polishing. A typical aggregate will charge up during daylight or under artificial light indoors and then glow for up to 10 hours depending on the grade of material. Figure 11.10 illustrates photoluminescent stones incorporated into a concrete pathway located in Dubai.

The active agent, strontium aluminate, is contained within resin or glass to form the aggregate. Aggregate sizes range from 4–15 mm, with glow colours ranging from blue to lime green. A fine sand product is also available for sealing in to existing

Figure 11.10 Exposed aggregate concrete incorporating AGT® Aqua Blue and Emerald Yellow Glow Stones, Dubai. Photograph: Courtesy of Ambient Glow Technology

surfaces. Typical external applications are footpaths, cycle tracks and landscape gardens. Internally photoluminescent concrete is used for polished work surfaces, floors and walls. The anticipated lifespan of the material is in excess of 20 years.

Smart Concrete

Concrete infused with potassium ions can store electricity for long periods.[60] The electricity could be stored when demand is low and then released at periods of peak demand. The novel potassium geopolymeric composite (KGP), developed by the University of Lancaster, is based on fly ash rather than Portland cement. The typical mix is fly ash with an alkaline activator of aqueous potassium silicate. The material works as a battery by the movement of the potassium ions within the crystalline matrix. In principle, within the domestic market, solar panels could generate electricity during daylight hours to charge up the concrete which would then be released and used as required. The system has the potential to store between 200 and 500 Watts per square metre. Urban street furniture such as street lights could be powered off-grid and large concrete buildings constructed with KGP concrete have the potential to store very significant quantities of electricity.

A significant side effect is that the KGP concrete is self-sensing. Changes in mechanical stress caused by cracking modify the electrical conductivity, so the system can be used as a diagnostic tool to check on the structural health of the concrete structure.

A further advance towards cement-based batteries by the University of Gothenburg[61] is the addition of 3 mm carbon fibres into the concrete mix to enhance conductivity. The system uses fine carbon-fibre mesh coated with iron for the anode and nickel for the cathode, which together prove more efficient than basic metal plates for the electrodes.

Bioreceptive Concrete

Bioreceptive concrete[62] is designed to encourage the growth of organisms such as moss, algae and lichens. The material is a hyperporous concrete which holds water like a sponge and therefore does not require watering to support poikilohydric organisms which absorb water from their general environment. These organisms absorb carbon dioxide and trap pollutants, purifying the air and providing habitat for small insects. Textured panels of Biocrete® with deep indents permit the rooting of larger plant species.

Photocatalytic Concrete

Photocatalytic concrete[63] contains catalysts to remove harmful pollutants by converting them into harmless agents or carbon dioxide and water. The most common catalytic agent is titanium dioxide (TiO_2) which, in the presence of sunlight, converts NO_2 to water-soluble nitrates.

Titanium Dioxide Surface Treatment

Concrete coated with water-based titanium dioxide (TiO_2) can improve urban air quality by removal of nitrogen oxides (NO_x) from the ambient air.[64] The titanium dioxide in the form of nanoparticles acts as a catalyst in sunlight to break down the noxious nitrogen oxides (mainly NO and NO_2) into nitrates. In addition, the surface treatment is self-cleaning as it acts to break down organic material such as fungi and algae into carbon dioxide and water.

Cob and Rammed-Earth Construction

Traditional cob construction[65] is being tested for durability and structural strength by the University of Plymouth with a new single-storey building. The local clay is blended with hemp rather than straw which was traditionally used. The environmental advantage of cob construction is the total elimination of the use of cement with its associated high embodied energy. Devon clay is ideal for cob construction as it is well-graded with a range of particle size from coarse gravel through fine sand to coarse clay. The material also has a low expansion and contraction which otherwise can cause cracking of the completed structure. Typical construction is a 450 mm stone plinth followed by lifts of 500 mm at a time. Deep eaves are necessary to prevent severe weathering of external walls which are normally finished with lime plaster. The hygroscopic properties of clay can moderate internal humidity, reducing the number of house dust mites and their associated allergies.

The ideal material for raw rammed-earth construction is a mixture of gravel, sand, silt and clay fines. The clay should be sufficient to act as an efficient binder, but not in excess to cause large moisture movement or cracking of the finished construction. If the local raw materials have insufficient binding properties then some Portland cement (5–8%) is added as a stabiliser. Alternative stabilisers include pozzolana, blast-furnace slag and coal ash. The material is built up in layers, typically 100–150 mm deep, within rigid formwork, which must be strong enough not to distort under manual or mechanical consolidation. Reinforcements including bamboo or steel rebar may be incorporated to enhance stability. Thick rammed-earth walls have a good thermal mass, giving temperature stability but relatively poor insulation unless augmented by the incorporation of an insulating layer, preferably using ecologically appropriate materials such as wood fibre or mycelium. Externally rammed earth can be finished with several coats of lime-wash. Only raw rammed earth can be fully recycled or composted, as stabilised rammed earth contains residues of the admixtures. However, stabilised rammed earth has only about half the carbon footprint of the equivalent concrete wall. Design detailing is important to ensure that rainwater does not run down the surface and cause deterioration.

3D-Printed Mineral Foam Construction

ETH Zürich is experimenting with the use of 3D-printing to build wall structures of lightweight insulating cement-free mineral foam[66] made from recycled waste. The mineral foam is extruded into hollow three-dimensional units which can be filled with mineral foam and sealed with plaster to create non-structural exterior walls. The foam can be applied in varying densities to optimise thermal or strength performance as necessary.

3D-Printed Clay Construction

Prototypical 3D-printed clay construction[67] has been experimented in Bologna, Italy, using clay from a nearby riverbed. The material has been named Tecla® from a combination of the words technology and clay. Construction involves the use of a modular 3D-printer with two synchronised arms each of which can work an area of $50m^2$. The production of a typical dome-form $60m^2$ housing module is highly efficient using only approximately 6 kilowatts of electricity during the 200-hour production process. The system has considerable potential for the rapid construction of housing in emergency or natural disaster areas.

References

1. *Low carbon concrete routemap – Setting the agenda for a path to net zero*, (https://www.ice.org.uk/), 2022, Institution of Civil Engineers, London.
2. *Emerging naterials: Ferrock*, Bonnefin, I., 18 November 2022, (https://www.certifiedenergy.com.au/emerging-materials/emerging-materials-ferrock/), New South Wales, Australia.
3. *Cemex inaugurates Climafuel at Rugby cement plant*, 1 June 2022, (https://www.cemfuels.com/news/item/3345/), Global CemFuels News, Pro Global Media Ltd., Epsom, Surrey.
4. Cemex UK Operations Ltd., (https://cemex.co.uk), Coventry.
5. *Fuel switching to hydrogen*, 10 August 2022, (https://www.hanson.co.uk/en/news-and-events/fuel-switching-to-hydrogen).
6. British Standard BS EN 197-5: 2021. *Cement. Portland-composite cement CEMII/C-M and Composite cement CEM VI*, BSI, London.
7. British Standard BS 8500: 2023. *Concrete. Complementary British Standard to BS EN 206. Part 1: Method of specifying and guidance for the specifier. Part 2: Specification for constituent materials and concrete.*, BSI, London.
8. *Vegetable Ashes as Supplementary Cementitious Materials* Martirena, F., and Monzo, J., Cement and Concrete Research Vol. 114, pp. 57–64, 2018, Science Direct, Elsevier, Amsterdam.
9. *Durian pectin and rice husk ash (RHA) as partial replacement of cement in concrete* Chia, S.L., Zamri, Z., Muniandy, A., Joseph, E., and Sathasivam, J., IOP Conference Series: Earth and Environmental Science, 476, 012022, 2020, IOP Publishing, Bristol.
10. *Earth Friendly Concrete*, (https://ukgbc.org/resources/earth-friendly-concrete/), 15 November 2022, UK Green Building Council, London.
11. PAS 8820: 2016 *Construction materials. Alkali-activated cementitious*

material and concrete. *Specification*, BSI, London.

12. *Vertua – Lower carbon concrete*, (https://www.cemex.co.uk/lower-carbon-concrete), Cemex, Coventry.

13. *The carbon neutral protocol 2023*, (www.climateimpact.com), January 2023, Climate Impact Partners Ltd., Oxford.

14. *Cemfree – Reducing concrete's carbon emissions with game-changing technology and dedicated R&D*, (https://www.cemfree.com), CemFree DB Group, Bourn, Cambridge.

15. *Eco-Cement*, (https://tececo.com/simple.eco-cement.php), TecEco Pty. Ltd., Sustainable Technologies, Tasmania, Australia.

16. *Liquid Granite Building Material of the Future Unveiled*, Science Daily, 4 November 2009, Sheffield Hallam University.

17. *Carbon negative cement*, Concrete Quarterly, 8 April 2022, MPA The Concrete Centre, London.

18. *Seratech*, (https://www.seratechcement.com/our-technology), Seratech, London.

19. *Cambridge electric cement*, Concrete quarterly, Summer 2023, Issue 283, MPA The Concrete Centre, London.

20. *Use of biochar as carbon sequestering additive in cement mortar*, Gupta, S., Kua, H.W. and Low, C.Y., Cement and Concrete Composites, Vol. 87, 2018, pp. 110–129 and Vol. 95, 2019 pp. 285-6, Elsevier, Amsterdam.

21. *Solidia – Sustainable cement manufacturing technology*, (https://solidiatech.com/solutions.html), Solidia Technologies, New Jersey, USA.

22. *CarbonBuilt – Ultra-low carbon concrete*, (https://carbonbuilt.com), Torrance, California, USA.

23. *CarbonCure's sustainable concrete solution*, (https://www.carboncure.com), Halifax, Nova Scotia, Canada.

24. *Scientists develop 'programmable' cement particles to attain enhanced properties*, 7 December 2016, Phys. org., Rice University, Houston.

25. *Carbon capture and storage (CCS)*, (https://www.heidelbergmaterials.com/en/carbon-capture-and-storage-ccs), Heidelberg Materials, Heidelberg, Germany.

26. *Net zero cement works at Padeswood one step closer following government announcement*, 30 March 2023, Hanson Heidelberg Cement Group, Maidenhead, Berkshire.

27. *Unlocking a low carbon future*, (https://hynet.co.uk), HyNet North West.

28. *Carbon-capturing algae*, Concrete Quarterly, Summer 2020, Issue No. 272, MPA The Concrete Centre, London.

29. *Brevik CCS – World's first CO2-capture facility at a cement plant*, (https://www.brevikccs.com/en), Heidelberg Materials, Heidelberg, Germany.

30. *Redefining carbon capture with ultra-efficient next-generation technology*, MOF Technologies / Nuada, (https://nuadaco2.com), Belfast.

31. *State of the art fuel mix for UK cement production to test the path for 'Net Zero': A technical, environmental and safety demonstration*, (https://assets.publishing.service.gov.uk/government/uploads/),

August 2022, Mineral Products Association, London.

32. *BES 6001 Framework standard for Responsible Sourcing. v.4.0*, 2022, British Standards Institution, London.

33. British Standard BS 8902: 2009. *Responsible sourcing sector certification schemes for construction products. Specification*, BSI, London.

34. *Meet the construction material of the future*, (https://basalt.tech), Bastech, Leighton Buzzard, Bedfordshire.

35. *Hemp rebar could offer low-cost alternative to steel*, The Concrete Times on Line, Callaghan, S., 22 March 2022, Ashford, Kent.

36. *Proposed design methodology for titanium reinforcing bars in concrete* Plat, S., and Harries, K., University of Bath, Engineering Structures, 178, pp. 543–553, 2019.

37. *The Cube will be 'world's first building made of carbon concrete*, Frearson, A. 30 July 2021, Dezeen, London.

38. *Investigation of bamboo as concrete reinforcement in the construction for low-cost housing industry* Rahim, N.L., Ibrahim, N.M., Salehuddin, S., Mohammed, S.A., and Othman, M.Z., 2020 IOP Conference Series – Earth and Environmental Science, 476, 012058, 2020, IOP Publishing, Bristol.

39. *Bamboo reinforced concrete: A critical review*, Archila, H., Kaminski, S., Trujillo, D., Escamilla, E.Z. and Harries, K.A., Materials and Structures, Vol. 51, Article No. 102, 2018, Springer Link, New York.

40. *Adfil – Manufacturing micro and macro fibres*, (https://adfil.com), Anglo-Danish Fibre Industries Ltd., Hull.

41. *Concretene – Graphene enhanced concrete* (https://www.nationwideengineering. co.uk/), Nationwide Engineering, Manchester.

42. *Recycled fibre reinforcement*, (https://www.zerowasteworks.co.uk), Zero Waste Works Ltd., Sheffield.

43. *Hemp Lime: An Introduction to low-impact building materials*, BRE Information Paper IP 14/11, IHS BRE Press, 2011, Bracknell.

44. *Low carbon futures*, (https://mirreco. com/wp-content/uploads/2019/04/ 02767-Mirreco-A4-Flyer.pdf), Mirreco Hemp Cast, Perth, Australia.

45. *Revolutionary hemp manufacturing*, (https://mirreco.com), Mirreco / Advanced Manufacturing Growth Centre Ltd., Perth, West Australia.

46. *Timbercrete: Components, advantages and applications*, (https://theconstructor.org), 13 July 2022, The Constructor, Sheffield.

47. *Sugarcrete – From agro-waste to sustainable structures: Concrete alternatives made from sugarcane*, 29 May 2023, ArchDaily, Santiago, Chile.

48. *Bendable concrete could make infrastructure safer – and cheaper*, Zeiba, D., 15 January 2019, The Architect's Newspaper, New York.

49. *Kiacrete – A new kind of permeable paving embeds recycled plastic tubes in a self-compacting cementitious material* Kia, A., Imperial College, London, Concrete Quarterly Issue No. 279, p. 6-7, Summer 2022, MPA The Concrete Centre, London.

50. *Advancements in bacteria based self-healing concrete and the promise of modelling* Bagga, M., Hamley-Bennett, C,

Alex, A. et al., Construction and Building Materials, Vol. 358, 5 December 2022, Science Direct, Elsevier, Amsterdam.

51. *Sensicrete-Self healing concrete*, (https://www.sensicon.co.uk/), Sensicon, Liverpool.

52. *Basilisk- Self-healing concrete*, (https://basiliskconcrete.com), Basilisk Self-healing Concrete, Delft, Netherlands.

53. *Biomineralization and Successive Regeneration of Engineered Living Building Materials*, Heveran, C. M., Williams, S.L., Qiu, J., Artier, J., Huber, M.H., Cook, S.M., Cameron, J. C. and Srubar, W.V., Matter, Vol. 2, Issue 2, pp. 481–494, February 2020, Cell Press, Science Direct, Elsevier.

54. *Concrete Canvas: Erosion control and containment*, (https://www.concretecanvas.com), Concrete Canvas Ltd., Pontyclun, Rhondda Cynon Taf, Wales.

55. *Development of electrically conductive concrete*. Cordon, H.C.F., Tadini, F.B., Akiyama, G.A., de Andrade, V.O., da Silva, R.C., Cerâmica Vol. 66, pp. 88–92, 2020, Brazil.

56. *Magnetizable concrete technology for wireless charging*, Power Electronics News, 23 March 2019, Aspencore Network, Cambridge, Massachusetts.

57. *Litracon light transmitting concrete*, Etherington, R., 20 January 2008, (https://www.dezeen.com), Dezeen, London.

58. *Light reflecting concrete*, (https://www.heringinternational.com/en/products-services/architectural-concrete/surface-design/lightreflectingconcrete), Hering Bau GmbH, Burbach, Germany.

59. *Ultra Grade Glow Stones*, (https://ambientglowtechnology.com), Ambient Glow Technology, Nebraska, USA.

60. *Inherently multifunctional geopolymeric cementitious composite as electrical energy storage and self-sensing structural material*, Saafi, A., Gullane, A., Huang, B., Sadeghi, H., Ye, J. and Sadeghi, F. Composite Structures, Vol. 201, pp. 766–778, 1 October 2018, Science Direct, Elsevier.

61. *Innovation: Cement based batteries*, Concrete Quarterly, Winter 2021, Issue 277, MPA The Concrete Centre, London.

62. *Bioreceptive concrete supports diversity*, MPA The Concrete Centre, London.

63. *Photocatalytic concrete*, Han, B., Zhang, L. and Ou, J., Smart and multifunctional concrete. Towards sustainable infrastructures, 2017, Springer, Singapore.

64. *Paints and surfaces for the removal of nitrogen oxides*, (http://uk-air.defra.gov.uk), 2016, Air Quality Expert Group, Department for Environment, Food and Rural Affairs, Gov.UK.

65. *CobBauge project* (https://www.cobbauge.eu/en/), June 2023, University of Plymouth.

66. *3D-printing lightweight, insulated walls using cement-free mineral foam*, Franco, J.T., 23 May 2023, Arch Daily, Santiago, Chile.

67. *Tecla house 3D-printed from locally sourced clay*, Parkes, J., 23 April 2021, Dezeen, London.

CHAPTER 12

Timber and Related Products

CONTENTS

Introduction

Timber, provided that it is from renewable sources accredited by PEFC® (Programme for the Endorsement of Forest Certification scheme) and/or FSC (Forest Stewardship Council), which certify responsible forestry harvesting, is clearly one of the most eco-friendly materials. Solid timber, laminated timber and the standard timber products such as plywood, particleboards and fibreboards are the well-established products and are described in standard texts. This chapter focuses on the more recently developed cross-laminated timber (CLT) and a range of modified timber products with specialist-enhanced properties. In addition, the timber alternatives – bamboo, hempwood and cardboard are described. However, many of these specialist products

DOI: 10.1201/9781003360469-12

are unlikely to become mainstream construction materials. The fire properties of timber are always a major consideration with respect to building construction.

Cross-Laminated Timber

Cross-Laminated Timber[1],[2] (CLT) is manufactured by laminating lengths of timber into large panels of any transportable shape and dimension for wall, floor and roof elements. Openings for doors, windows, stairs and service ducts can be incorporated into the factory-produced sections using CNC routers which can work to fine tolerances. Most CLT is manufactured from softwood grades within the range of C24–C16. Thicknesses normally range between 50 mm to 300 mm, but panels up to 500 mm can be manufactured. It is typically manufactured from three to a maximum of seven layers. The timber used is kiln dried to a moisture content of 12% to prevent pest and fungal attack. The cross-lamination controls thermal and moisture movement, giving a dimensionally more stable product than standard solid timber. A range of adhesives are used in the manufacturing process and formaldehyde-free units can be supplied if required. Spruce, larch, fir and pine are the standard timbers used. The outer layers may be of either orientation and a range of surface-quality finishes are available according to the particular application.

The typical thermal conductivity of commercial cross-laminated timber systems is 0.13 W/mK. A typical cavity construction using 100 mm CLT with an internal service void of 25 mm and 12 mm plasterboard requires 100 mm of mineral wool insulation with 102.5 mm brick cladding to achieve a U-value of 0.30 W/m^{2}K.

The timber used should be harvested from sustainable forests and certified by the FSC or PFEC schemes. Clearly using timber has the ecological advantage of sequestering carbon within the building rather than emitting carbon in the manufacture of the other standard construction materials. At the end of the useful life of the building, timber can be recycled or used as biomass fuel.

Timber, as a combustible material, cannot be used in the external walls of certain classes of buildings over 11 m in height. Only materials classified as A1 or A2-s0,d0 to BS EN 13501–1: 2018[3] are permitted. As with all timber products, increased fire resistance can be achieved by the application of coatings or impregnation. The design of CLT construction must take into consideration the reaction to fire as well as fire resistance. Some debonding can occur under fire conditions which may affect structural strength. External timber requires cladding or render to provide a weatherproof envelope.

The Charlton Workstack in Greenwich (Figure 12.1) is a development of 14 light industrial and office units spread over 5 floors. The units, designed by dRMM Architects in conjunction with Greenwich Enterprise Board, are constructed in cross-laminated timber (CLT). The design has a progressive 1.7 m cantilever at each floor to give shading and reduced solar gain to

Figure 12.1 The Charlton Workstack. Designed by dRMM Architects in conjunction with Arup Structural Engineers. Photograph: Arthur Lyons

the lower levels, but provides large west-facing windows to provide good natural light. This design detail is achievable due to the inherent strength of CLT. Disabled parking and electric car charging points are provided.

The Black and White 17.8 m building[4] (Figure 12.2) by Waugh Thistleton Architects for TOG (The Office Group) is constructed from CLT slabs with beech laminated veneer lumber (LVL) for the column and beam frame. The exterior is clad with glulam[5] curtain walling. The full-height louvres provide natural shade, reducing solar gain on the façade while enhancing the natural light reaching the

Figure 12.2 Exterior of the Black & White Building designed by Waugh Thistleton Architects for TOG (The Office Group). Photograph: Courtesy of Jake Curtis

interior spaces. Figure 12.3 illustrates the basic form of construction, and Figure 12.4 illustrates an example of the high-quality interior spaces.

Hardwood Laminated Veneer Lumber

Until recently laminated veneer lumber (LVL) was exclusively manufactured from softwood. However, a recent development in Germany is the production of hardwood laminated veneer lumber using beech timber.[6] This gives the potential to extend multi-storey post and beam construction further than would be feasible with softwood laminated veneer lumber.

The timber for hardwood laminated veneer lumber, BauBuche®, is sustainably harvested beech from the extensive forests

Figure 12.3 The Black & White building under construction illustrates the beech laminated veneer lumber (LVL) frame and cross-laminated timber (CLT) slabs. Photograph: Courtesy of TOG

of Germany within 150–200 km of the sawmill.[5] It is fully certified to PEFC® (Programme for the Endorsement of Forest Certification scheme) requirements to ensure continuity of supply and ultimate sustainability. To produce the laminated product, beech timber is rotary peeled and then laminated with the veneers predominantly aligned parallel to the grain to maximise strength in the load-bearing direction. The veneers are glued with phenolic resin and pressed at 100°C to ensure uniformity and adhesion. As phenolic resin adhesive is used no noxious formaldehyde is evolved in the process. To produce column and beam sections the sheet material is cut to appropriate widths and then further laminated as in the production of standard glued laminated

timber. The material is finally sanded to produce a high-quality surface finish.

Apart from its environmental credentials, hardwood laminated veneer lumber has physical properties which allow it to compete with other traditional materials. BauBuche® has a compressive strength equivalent to C50/60 concrete, so it can be used for columns of similar dimensions to reinforced concrete but with a lower dead weight. The material is manufactured to lengths of 18 m for boards and beams with a maximum width of 680 mm for panels.

BauBuche® is categorised to glulam strength class GL75 compared to typical homogeneous glulam strengths ranging up to GL32 to BS EN 14080: 2013.[7] The fire classification of the material to BS EN 13501–1: 2018 is Euroclass D-s2,d0[8] but

Figure 12.4 Interior of the Black & White building illustrating the high-quality exposed woodwork. Photograph: Courtesy of Jake Curtis

this can be enhanced to B-s1, d0 when treated with an appropriate fire-retardant coating.

Recycling Timber

According to the Wood Recyclers' Association (WRA), the UK generates approximately 4.5 million tonnes of timber waste annually.[9] Of this approximately, 26% is recycled into board manufacture, 63% is converted into biomass and the remainder is either exported or used as animal bedding or for horticultural purposes. According to TRADA[10] (Timber Research and Development Association), only 1% of timber waste now enters landfill sites generating the greenhouse gas methane as it degrades.

Researchers at Flinders University, Adelaide, Australia,[11] have developed a method of recycling wood chips into a timber product with all the characteristics of a natural tropical hardwood. The process involves mixing wood waste with a water-based nano-glue to produce a product which replicates the properties of a mature natural hardwood. The process can reproduce many wood types including various international species. Currently, the product is used in Australia for indoor furniture, but it is projected to have production units alongside international LVL and plywood manufacturers to take their waste for immediate conversion into Smartwood®. Current research is investigating enhancements to give fire, water and termite resistance without the use of harmful chemicals.

Figure 12.5 illustrates the good reuse of timber railway sleepers for balustrades in two-storey apartments.

Chemically Modified Timber

Chemical modification of timber involves the impregnation of permeable species of wood with chemical reagents which interact with the free hydroxyl groups within the cellulose macromolecules. Processes involve pressure treatment with either acetic anhydride for acetylation (Accoya®)[12] or furfuryl alcohol for furfurylation (Kebony®).[13] After impregnation, the timber is heated to activate the reaction between the water-binding sites in the wood cell walls and the modification chemical.

The modified timber with a reduced number of free hydroxyl groups has significantly reduced water absorption and thus

Figure 12.5 Recycling of timber railway sleepers as a balustrades in a small development of holiday residences in Kato Zakros, Crete. Photograph: Arthur Lyons

greater dimensional stability. For a timber such as radiata pine, a maximum moisture content of approximately 6% is achieved by acetylation with no colour change, producing a timber durable to Class 1. The chemical processes do not significantly affect the key physical properties of the timber, but reduce warping and splintering. They also produce increased resistance to biological deterioration and insect attack including termites. Kebony® is predominantly manufactured from radiata pine, but is also made from southern yellow pine and Scots pine. The furfurylation process significantly darkens the colour of the wood. Acetylation has no effect on the colour of the timber, but

Accoya® contains acetic anhydride, which may give a vinegar-like smell for a short period of time. Accoya® (Figure 12.6) is guaranteed for 50 years above ground and for 25 years in fresh water. It is accredited by the FSC® (Forest Stewardship Council) and has Cradle to Cradle Gold® certification for sustainability. Figure 12.7 illustrates the use of Accoya® as an external cladding material in a large building in Riga, Latvia.

Heat Treated Timber

Heat-treated wood,[14] such as Thermowood®, is softwood that has been specially treated at

Figure 12.6 Typical range of colours for Accoya® – chemically modified timber. Photograph: Arthur Lyons

Figure 12.7 Mežaparka Birojs Building in Riga, Latvia, externally clad in Accoya®. Building design by Didrihsons Architects. Photograph: Copyright to Accsys® 2023 – SBM Fastwood

temperatures in the range of 160°C to 210°C in a reduced oxygen atmosphere, steam or oil. The process makes a permanent change to the chemical structure of the wood, reducing the equilibrium moisture content by up to 50%, expelling resin and breaking down some of the natural sugars. The timber becomes more durable and stable, taking on many of the performance characteristics and darker colour of a hardwood. It is particularly suitable for exterior cladding, decking, windows, doors, garden furniture and any products affected by harsh climatic conditions.

Typically, shrinkage and swelling are reduced by up to 50% and the increased resistance to fungal attack leads to lower maintenance costs. As with untreated timber,

Thermowood® can be coated with oil, water or solvent-based finishes to protect it from UV light, but externally, if untreated, it will eventually turn silver-grey. Thermowood® should not be used in ground contact and may have a slightly reduced mechanical strength compared to the equivalent untreated timber. Typically durability for exterior use is 30 years. The University of Leicester John Foster Hall of Residence (Figures 12.8 and 12.9) is clad in Thermowood for aesthetic and durability reasons.

A slightly different product, Rhino Wood®, is softwood which has been heat treated followed by impregnation with wax.[15] The material has dimensional stability and greater strength than the South

Figure 12.8 Thermally modified timber cladding. University of Leicester student accommodation. Architects: Goddard Manton. Photograph: Arthur Lyons

African pine starting material. The product has a Class 1 durability rating with respect to moisture.

Densified Wood

Densified wood[16] is three times as dense as the untreated material with greatly enhanced stiffness and compressive strength. It is also moisture, scratch and impact resistant. The process of densification involves boiling the timber in sodium hydroxide (NaOH) and sodium sulphite (Na_2SO_3) to partially remove the lignin and hemicellulose, which stiffen the natural cell wall structure. The material is then compressed to one-fifth of its size to collapse the cell walls, followed by gentle heating at 65°C to activate the formation of chemical bonding between the adjacent cellulose molecules. The densified wood is about three times the density of the untreated material, fifty times more resistant to compression and twenty times as stiff. Densified wood can be moulded to any

Figure 12.9 Detail of thermally modified timber. Photograph: Arthur Lyons

shape and is moisture-resistant. The material has the potential to be a significant construction material in competition with steel and titanium alloys.

Transparent Wood

Wood can be made to permit light transmission by removal of the lignin content which absorbs light and gives it the brown colouration.[17] The hollow cellulose fibres also scatter light reducing transparency. One process to remove the lignin involves boiling and bleaching thin timber sections with hydrogen peroxide to extract the lignin, making the timber white rather than brown. The timber is then put under a vacuum, followed by impregnation with epoxy or methyl methacrylate resin to restore strength and give partial transparency. In the future, recyclable plastic rather than petrochemical-based products will be used. An alternative process involves brushing the hydrogen peroxide onto the wood followed by light activation. A further process involves compressing wood veneer to remove the lignin followed by polymer impregnation making the wood 85% transparent. Transparent wood is tough and can withstand ten times more stress and four times more strain than normal wood.

Flexible Wood

Flexible wood (Woodolex®) (Figure 12.10) is a form of MDF manufactured from 96% recycled wood and 4% adhesive.[18] The strip material can be bent into any form by the application of heat, typically with an electric heat gun which is applied for approximately 10–15 minutes. The wood is then bent into the required shape and held until it has cooled down. Flexible wood is available as plain strip or in profiled forms for skirtings and architraves. The material can be processed by all standard woodworking tools.

Timber Terrazzo

Timber terrazzo,[19] Foresso®, is made from waste wood which would normally be burned. The sheet material can be used for worktops and a range of interior surfaces. Waste wood chips and wood dust are mixed with a mineral binder of cement and plaster

Figure 12.10 Woodolex® flexible wood. Photograph: Arthur Lyons

which is incorporated to give durability and a fine finish. The mix is blended with a VOC and formaldehyde-free resin and laid to a 6 mm layer onto 18 mm plywood.

The range of background colours for the wood chip variety is brown, green, beige and charcoal. These colours are also available without the incorporation of wood chips (Figure 12.11). The maximum sheet size is 3050 × 1220 mm. The material can be cut, drilled, routed, sanded and glued as for timber.

(a)

(b)

(c)

(d)

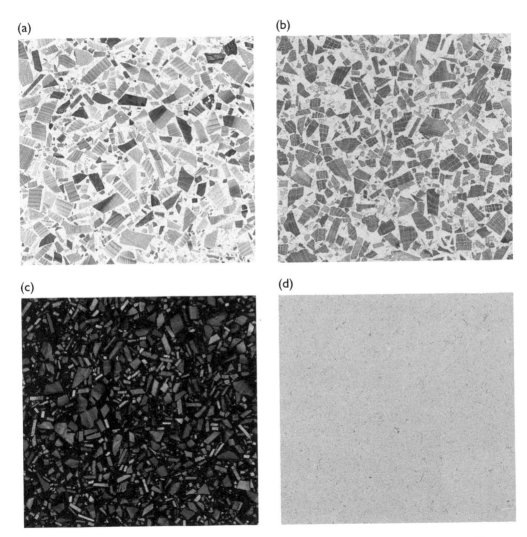

Figure 12.11 (a–d) Foresso® timber terrazzo surface detail images. (a). Ivory cedar and walnut, (b). Azure oak, (c). Charcoal walnut, (d). Azure no-chip. Photographs: Courtesy of Foresso Co. UK

Bamboo

Bamboo, when supported by Forest Stewardship Council's® chain of custody certification, is a highly environmentally friendly material. Bamboo can grow two metres in six months, and if correctly harvested, it is a fully sustainable material. Traditional wood has a harvesting cycle of at least 25 years compared to 3 years for bamboo. It is one of the fastest-growing plants in the world and is biodegradable. Bamboo plantations produce significantly more oxygen than traditional forests and the *Guadua* species which is cultivated in Latin America can sequester up to 360 tons/hectare/year of CO_2.

Bamboo has been used structurally for several major projects including the Garden Pavilion at the 2019 International Horticultural Exhibition in Yangqing, Beijing, China[20] (Figure 12.12). The structure was made from over 5000 lengths of 80–100 mm bamboo, which were fire-baked and bent to form the 32 m arch structure reaching a height of 9 metres. The structure has an anticipated lifespan of 30 years.

A further building of architectural interest constructed in bamboo is the Sports Hall for Panyaden International School in Thailand[21] (Figure 12.13). The 782 sq.m. hall, built in 2017, has space for volleyball, badminton and basketball. The prefabricated trusses, which were prebuilt on site and craned into position, span over 17 m and were built without steel reinforcements or connections. The

Figure 12.12 The INBAR (International Organisation for Bamboo and Rattan) Bamboo Eye Pavilion, Yangqing district, Beijing, China. Architects: Studio Cardenas Conscious Design, Milan. Photograph: Courtesy of Pan Zhenyu

Figure 12.13 Sports Hall for Panyaden International School, Thailand. Architects: Chiangmai Life Construction. Photograph: Courtesy of Alberto Cosi/Italian Connection

building has an anticipated lifespan of 50 years. The sports hall carbon footprint is zero as the growing bamboo absorbed more CO_2 during its growth than was emitted during subsequent treatment, transportation and construction.

Flooring tongue & groove units (Figure 12.14) are manufactured from horizontal or vertical strips of bamboo and also from compressed random strands. Colours range from natural, through grey, to a selection of light and dark browns. The surface, either as strip or parquet block, is hard-wearing and can be coated in a non-slip finish. The material is also appropriate for wall coverings and countertops.

Structural Engineered Bamboo (SEB) or GluBam[22] is similar to standard Laminated Veneer Lumber (LVL). It is manufactured by gluing and hot-pressing the raw bamboo culms (woody stems) to produce a laminate. The production of GluBam sheets is similar to the manufacture of plywood. The bamboo culms are laid out as a mat and hot-pressed with adhesive. The higher grade material for GluBam (SEB) sections is made just with the outer fibrous material by removing the lower strength interior of the culm before lamination. The material is stronger than glulam in compression and ten times stronger in tension due to the silica fibre content. The high density promotes good bolted connections as the material is less susceptible to crushing than standard timber. The main applications of SEB are columns, beams, curtain walling and framing.

Figure 12.14 A range of bamboo flooring manufactured by The Bamboo Flooring Company, Leicester. Photograph: Arthur Lyons

Bamboo also has applications in exterior landscaping as illustrated in Figure 12.15.

HempWood

Already hemp has become a familiar material in the context of hempcrete, but hemp also has the potential to be an alternative to wood. Hemp can be cultivated in three to four months and it absorbs more than 20 tonnes of carbon per hectare, more than four times the equivalent forest. It can also produce two crops annually, increasing its environmental credentials.

The raw hemp can be converted into hempwood (Figure 12.16) by heating followed by compression with soy-based

Figure 12.15 Bamboo as a garden screen, Perth, West Australia. Photograph: Arthur Lyons

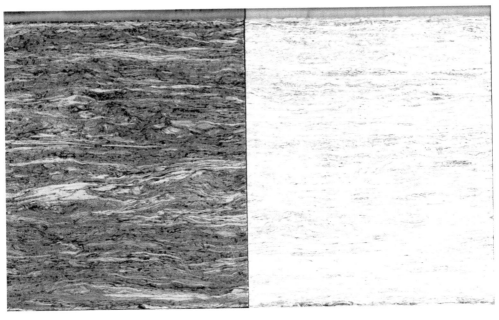

Figure 12.16 Samples of hempwood illustrating colour and graining effect. Photograph: Arthur Lyons

adhesive or wood glue.[23] The strong material can be cut, worked, sanded and finished like hardwood. Currently, prototype hempwood is produced in lengths only up to two metres and is suitable only for internal use. An alternative system produces hemp OSB. Hemp-based materials have great potential, particularly in the housing market, where framing elements and structural panels could be manufactured from hempwood and hemp OSB. The use of these materials could significantly speed up the shift towards net-zero carbon in the construction industry.

Cardboard Tubes

Cardboard tubes are now an accepted structural material. The material was pioneered by the Japanese architect Shigeru Ban in the 1990s for small structures (Figure 12.17), but over the last two decades, the material has been successfully used for the construction of many significant buildings, including the Christchurch Cathedral in New Zealand (Figure 12.18) following the disastrous earthquake in 2011, a footbridge in France and a theatre in Amsterdam. The cathedral in Christchurch, which accommodates a congregation of 700,

Figure **12.17** Cardboard tube structure at Pouilly-en-Auxois, France. Architect: Shigeru Ban, Photograph: Arthur Lyons

Figure 12.18 Christchurch Cathedral, New Zealand. Structure built with cardboard tubes. Architect Shigeru Ban. Photograph: Courtesy of Linda Bone and Brenda Griffiths

is constructed from a series of interlocking 600 mm tubes each weighing 120 kg that are coated with polyurethane waterproofing and flame retardant. The building is expected to last for 50 years. Meanwhile, the original stone cathedral built in 1881 is under repair with an anticipated finish date of 2027. Shigeru Ban has also used the material to build many temporary housing projects following natural disasters in Haiti, Rwanda and Japan.

The cardboard construction tubes are manufactured by gluing together spiralled layers of paper using PVA or starch adhesive. Fixings are purpose-built metal nodes bolted to the tube ends. Cardboard is naturally hygroscopic so it is necessary to protect it from warm moist internal environments and externally from rain. Ultimately the material can easily be recycled into new cardboard providing that only ecological fire-retardants have been applied. Cardboard tubes for structural use are not currently listed within the British Standards.

Durable MDF

Medite Tricoya® is a highly durable MDF panel manufactured from acetylated wood fibre with a 50-year guarantee above ground and 25 years below ground.[24] It has enhanced dimensional stability, durability and fungal resistance compared to standard MDF. It is suitable for internal and external use as a non-structural material, having a durability Class 1 equivalent to that of teak. The material has the same physical properties as standard medium-density fibreboards for fixing and machining.

Panel sizes	Thickness
1220 × 2440 mm	4, 6, 9, 12, 15, 18 mm
1220 × 3050 mm	12, 15, 18 mm

Formaldehyde-Free OSB

Medite Smartply® is manufactured from oriented timber strands without the use of formaldehyde-based resin which is normally the bonding agent within standard OSB.[25] The resin used reacts with the timber to a depth greater than 0.3 mm forming a chemical bond rather than the mechanical bonding produced by formaldehyde-based adhesives. It is available as OSB3 and the higher strength OSB4. The higher grade can be used in Service Class 2 conditions (heavy-duty load-bearing panel in humid conditions)

as defined by BS EN 1995-1-1: 2004 + A2: 2014 Eurocode 5.[26] It is however not water-proof and will not withstand prolonged exposure to water. Tongue and groove panels are available.

Panel size	Thickness
1220 × 2440 mm	16, 18, 22 mm
3297 × 1197 mm	12.5 mm

Special sizes up to 2.8 × 7.5 m × 40 mm are potentially available.

Particle Board with Lignin Binder

Traditional particle board is commonly bonded with fossil-based binders – typically urea formaldehyde or melamine urea form-aldehyde, but lignin binders offer an eco-alternative eliminating the risk of evolution of noxious formaldehyde vapour.[27] The physical properties of the particle board in relation to strength and water resistance are unaffected.

Recycled Paper Boards

Honext® fibreboard panels[28] (Figure 12.19) are manufactured from the upcycled waste fibres in paper mill sludge which otherwise would end up in landfill. The fibres from recycled paper and cardboard are too short to be reformed into paper, but can be reformed into construction boards for internal partitioning or cladding. The cellulose fibres are mixed with enzymes which ensure better bonding between the short fibres, which otherwise would require the addition of non-recyclable resins. Non-toxic additives are

Figure 12.19 Selection of recycled fibreboard panels made from paper mill sludge. Photograph: Arthur Lyons

incorporated to enhance the board's UV resistance. The slurry of 50–75% paper sludge and 25–50% waste cardboard is compressed and then passed through a drying tunnel. The product is non-toxic, contains no VOCs and is fully recyclable according to Circular Economy principles with a cradle-to-cradle certified silver classification. The material is water vapour and moisture-resistant and one grade (FR-B) has a fire classification of B-s1,d0, suitable for wall cladding in public spaces. It is lighter than MDF and has good sound-absorbing properties.

Richlite® paper board[29] is manufactured in the USA from recycled waste paper and cardboard which is reconverted into paper and then laminated into construction board. In the process, recycled paper is cut into sheets, soaked with phenolic resin, stacked in alternating directions of the paper and then heat pressed to set the thermosetting resin. When cooled a solid sheet material is produced. The resin has low VOCs and no formaldehyde. The product can be worked by milling and sanding as for hardwood. It has low water absorption and good heat resistance. Typical panel thicknesses range from 6 mm to 75 mm with sheet sizes up to 3660 × 1525 mm. Finishes are either mill, leathered or honed and colours range from light tan to dark brown and black. The material is suitable for a range of interior applications including worktops and cladding.

Alang-Alang

Alang-Alang[30] (Figures 12.20 and 12.21) is a type of grass used as a decorative roofing material mainly in the southern hemisphere. It is a natural grass grown on the islands around Bali and is typically used for thatching gazebos and garden huts. It is sold on bamboo battens for immediate use as a roofing material. It is only semi-durable lasting for 8–10 years under normal external

Figure 12.20 Alang-Alang roofing material. Interior view. Photograph: Arthur Lyons

Figure 12.21 Alang-Alang detail, Perth, West Australia. Photograph: Arthur Lyons

exposure conditions. Typical units are 2.5 m long with an 800 mm thatch overhang.

Fire Properties of Timber

Following the Grenfell fire disaster in 2017, the regulations relating to flammable materials, particularly for the cladding of high-rise buildings over 11 m in height, have been tightened. The Building Regulations Approved Document B[31] requires all materials that form part of an external wall of relevant buildings, including residential purpose groups, over 11 m in height must conform to the European fire classification of A1 or A2-s1,d0. The European classification incorporates a comprehensive range of factors including ignitability, flame spread, heat release, smoke production, also propensity for producing flaming droplets and particles. Materials classified as Euroclass B to F are considered combustible.

Many fire-retardant treatments are well-established for timber and timber products. A recent development has been the formulation of a fire-retardant (Burnblock®) based on 100% natural ingredients and 100% biodegradable. The material is pH-neutral with very low VOCs. Timber cladding treated under high pressure with this product can achieve a Euroclass B-s1,d0 rating for use internally or externally.

References

1. *Cross-laminated timber, An introduction to low-impact building materials*, BRE IP 17/11, Sutton, A., Black, D. and Walker, P., IHS BRE Press, Watford.
2. *Cross laminated timber: Introduction for specifiers* Wood Information Sheet WIS 2/3-61, 2016, BM TRADA, High Wycombe.
3. British Standard BS EN 13501-1: 2018. *Fire classification of construction products and building elements. Classification using data from reaction to fire tests*, BSI, London.
4. *I want to caress the lift!* (https://www.theguardian.com/artanddesign/2023/jan/30/caress-lift-eco-office-block/), 31 Jan 2023, The Guardian, London.
5. *Glued laminated timber* Wood Information Sheet WIS 1-6, 2016, BM TRADA, High Wycombe.
6. *BauBuche – Hardwood laminated veneer limber* (https://pollmeier.com/baubuche/), Pollmeier Massivholz Gmbh & Co., Creuzburg.
7. British Standard BS EN 14080: 2013. *Timber Structures. Glued laminated timber and glued solid timber. Requirements*, BSI, London.
8. European Reaction to Fire Classification (EuroClass) A1 – non-combustible, A2 limited combustibility.
9. *Waste wood assessment guidance for the UK waste wood industry*, Wood Recyclers' Association Ltd., version 2, November 2021, Inkberrow, Worcestershire.
10. *Recovering and minimising waste wood*, Wood Information Sheet WIS 2/3-59, 2020, BM TRADA, High Wycombe.
11. *Waste wood into forms of tropical hardwood*, The Lead, Adelaide, 21 May 2020.
12. *Ultra-high performance sustainable wood* (https://www.accoya.com/uk/), Accsys, London.
13. *Natural wood made to last* (https://kebony.com/), Kebony, Oslo.
14. *Modified Wood Products*, Wood Information Sheet WIS 2/3-63, 2021, BM TRADA, High Wycombe.
15. *Rhino wood comes to the UK market*, 6 September 2022, Premier Construction News, Manchester.
16. *New densified wood is as strong as steel*, Doyle, A., 12 February 2018, The Chemical Engineer, Rugby.
17. *Transparent wood is coming and it could make an energy-efficient alternative to glass*, Eichorn, S., The Conversation, 10 February 2021, The University of Bristol.
18. *Easy bend wooden board* (https://woodolex.cm), Greenford, West London.
19. *Renewed materials. Remade surfaces* (https://foresso.co.uk), Foresso, Birmingham.
20. *INBAR Garden Pavilion / Studio Cardenas Conscious Design*, Pintos P., 11 July 2019, ArchDaily, New York.
21. *Bamboo Sports Hall for Panyaden International School / Chiangmai Life Construction*, Castro, F., 5 September 2021, ArchDaily, New York.
22. *Glue Laminated Bamboo (GluBam) for Structural Applications*, Xiao, Y., Shan,

B., Yang, R.Z., Li, Z. and Chen, J., In *'Materials and Joints in Timber Structures'* pp. 589–601, Rilem Bookseries 9, Aicher, S., Reinhardt, H.-W., Garrecht, H. (Eds.), 2014.

23. *Hemp: The Next Disruptor in Construction after Wood?*, Brownell, B., 28 October 2021, Architect Magazine, (https://www.architectmagazine.com), Journal of the American Institute of Architects, Washington, USA.

24. *Medite Tricoya Extreme* (https://mdfosb.com/en/products/medite-tricoya-extreme), Medite Smartply, Dartford.

25. *Medite Smartply defines the standard of innovative wood-based panels* (https://mdfosb.com/en), Medite Smartply, Dartford.

26. British Standard BS EN 1995-1-1: 2004 + A2: 2014. *Eurocode 5: Design of timber structures. General. Common rules and rules for buildings*, BSI, London.

27. *Lignin-containing p-MDI binder for wood particle production*, Sumerskii, I., Solt-Rindler, P., van Herwijnen, H., Sulaeva, I. et al., October 2022, ResearchGate, Berlin.

28. *Honext – Circular materials for the built environment* (https://honextmaterial.com), Barcelona.

29. *Richlite solid paper composite* (https://www.surfacematter.co.uk), London.

30. *Bali's traditional roofing: The Alang-Alang thatch roof* (https://pablolunastudio.com/balis-traditional-roofing-the-alang-alang-thatch-roof/).

31. The Building Regulations Part B 2010 – Amendments to the Approved Documents – June 2022.

CHAPTER 13

Ferrous and Non-ferrous Metals

CONTENTS

Introduction

The steel industry, as one of the main producers of carbon dioxide is seeking alternative production techniques to achieve a low-carbon footprint by 2050. According to its decarbonisation action plan, British Steel aims to deliver an 82% reduction in carbon intensity by 2035.

Alternative fuels, carbon capture and more intensive recycling are clearly on the agenda.

Recent innovations in the steel industry include 3D printing and capitalising on the increased fire resistance of galvanized steel over the standard product. For non-ferrous metals, aluminium foam is a new material with good

DOI: 10.1201/9781003360469-13

thermal and acoustic insulating properties. The anti-microbial properties of copper can be used in the context of health-care services to reduce the spread of infections, particularly where surfaces are constantly being touched by staff and patients.

Steel Production

Currently steel production is responsible for approximately 8% of global CO_2 emissions. (1 tonne of steel produces approximately 1.9 tonnes of CO_2 according to World Steel Association 2022 data[1]). European steel is lower carbon than that produced in the UK as 80% of UK steel is produced by the traditional basic oxygen furnace, whereas in Europe a higher proportion of steel is produced by electric arc furnace. Electric arc furnace (EAF) production uses 100% recycled material compared to only 30% recycled content in the basic oxygen furnace (BOF) and therefore EAF production has a carbon footprint of around 20% that of BOF steelmaking and only about one-third the embodied energy. European manufacturers are committed to reduce emissions by 35% by 2030 and be carbon neutral by 2050. British Steel, according to its Decarbonisation Action Report, 2023,[2] is anticipating an 82% reduction in carbon by 2035 on the route to net zero by 2050. With the decarbonising of the national electricity grid, more opportunity will be available in the UK to produce genuinely low-carbon steel by the electric arc furnace method from scrap. One manufacturer, ArcelorMittal®, already uses 100% green electricity from solar and wind power with up to 100% recycled scrap to produce very low embodied carbon steel. Other manufacturers are increasingly producing certified lower CO_2 embodied steels.

According to the World Steel Association, currently 70% of global steel is produced by the basic oxygen furnace (BOF) system and 30% by the electric arc furnace (EAF) method.

The UK constructional steelwork market is worth approximately £1.6bn per year with consumption at approximately 0.8 million tonnes. Total UK steel production is around 7.2 million tonnes per annum which represents 0.4% of global production.[3] The market share for single-storey (warehouse) type buildings is 98%, and generally 65% for the non-domestic buildings market. For these reasons the steel industry is researching alternative lower carbon manufacturing processes. World annual production of virgin steel for all purposes is over 1.9 billion tonnes, with China producing approximately 57% of the total.

Steel Recycling and Reuse

Recycling plays an important part of the circular economy. The scrap network recycles 99% of all UK structural steel sections of which 13% are immediately reused. The repurposing of steel sections reduces the carbon impact by up to 80% compared to smelting and reforming. However, the large balance of scrap is returned to the steel producers. Steel has the advantage that it is infinitely recyclable. Repurposing unused steel stock can also reduce waste. However, the production of new steel in the traditional blast furnace using iron ore, coke (from coking coal) and limestone is energy-intensive and produces large quantities of CO_2.

Currently, the reuse of steel sections has significant risks for the developer, but the British Constructional Steelwork Association (BCSA) has published a model specification for the purchase of reclaimed steel sections[4]. The proposed business model involves the demolition contractor, the steel stockholder and the contractor who fabricates the reclaimed steelwork to the required standards.

A proportion of repurposed material is currently used for temporary steelwork. The Steel Construction Institute (SCI) gives guidance on this issue.[5]

Steel Specification

All structural steelwork should be procured by procedures as defined by BES 6001[6] (BRE Environmental & Sustainability Standard – Framework Standard for Responsible Sourcing, 2016) with the supplier following the management system BS EN ISO 14001[7] (Environmental management systems, Requirements with guidance for use, 2015). Waste should be minimised by direct ordering from the steel mills to avoid offcuts. Where offcuts are produced these should be reused elsewhere whenever possible rather than sent to scrap for recycling. Over-specification should be avoided and the design should facilitate flexibility and adaptability for future needs. Full details of the as-built structure should be recorded to permit reuse of the steelwork when the building is ultimately decommissioned. The

British Constructional Steelwork Association has published a sustainability specification[8] which requires Environmental Product Declarations (EPDs) to be submitted for all steel products.

Alternative Manufacturing Fuels

A 20% reduction in carbon emissions can be achieved by using hydrogen rather than pulverised coal injection (PCI) in a traditional blast furnace. However, coke is still required for reducing the iron ore (iron oxide) into iron. An intermediate process involves the use of natural gas, coke oven gas or biomass as alternatives to PCI to reduce the coke input with some reduction in CO_2 emissions.

A more fundamental development is the reduction of pelletized iron ore with natural gas or hydrogen within a DRI (Direct Reduced Iron) plant.[9] The reduction of iron ore to iron takes place below the melting point of iron so less heat energy is consumed. The process using natural gas is well developed, and in 2021 the first 100 tonnes of hydrogen-reduced sponge iron was produced in Sweden. The hydrogen reduction process is dependent on the availability of green hydrogen, produced from renewable energy sources by the electrolysis of water, which is currently expensive but may halve over the next 10 years. However, Sweden has extensive access to large quantities of renewable hydro and wind power and H_2GreenSteel®[10] uses hydropower from the Lule River to power the electrolysis process which will generate green hydrogen on site in Bowden. Full steel production will commence in 2025. The hydrogen process reduces the CO_2 emissions from 1600kg/tonne to 25 kg/tonne of crude steel. The pelletized iron is then heated and liquefied together with steel scrap in an electric arc furnace (EAF) to produce standard steel. The second process does not lead to any carbon emissions assuming that the electricity is obtained from renewable sources.

A further potential reduction in carbon emissions within the steel industry is switching from natural gas to hydrogen as a fuel source in the re-heating furnaces. Currently this approach is being tested in Teesside alongside wind farm and solar-generated electricity, which powers the electrolyser producing green hydrogen.

Current research in Ghent[11] is assessing the viability of converting waste wood, agricultural waste and end-of-life plastics into biofuels to replace fossil fuels in the steelmaking process. ArcelorMittal® is experimenting with using a heliogen to harness solar energy by using a field of mirrors to concentrate and capture sunlight which will then be converted into heat, electricity or clean fuels for use in steel manufacturing which would then be carbon-neutral.

Ultimately the steel industry will have to use strictly monitored carbon offsetting to account for its residual emissions.

Carbon Capture

Carbon capture and use (CCU)[12] plays an important role in the decarbonising of steel production, where blast furnace CO_2 is either captured and trapped in geological formations (CCS – carbon capture and storage) or used (CCU) in the production of ethanol and plastics by gas-fermentation technology.[13] Any unavoidable carbon emissions can be offset through approved offsetting schemes. Heat recovery systems can be used for electricity generation thus reducing external grid requirements.

In the very long term, it is anticipated that all traditional blast furnaces, even with carbon capture, use and storage (CCUS) will be decommissioned and replaced with hydrogen-reduced DRI (Direct Reduced Iron). Also, eventually, the demand for new steel will reduce as more scrap becomes available. Furthermore, designs will necessarily incorporate demountability enabling the direct reuse of steel members.

The 1st edition of the 'Sustainability Specification' for structural steelwork[14] includes guidance on both the design and fabrication of structural steelwork and also information on Environmental Product Declarations (EPDs).

Molten Oxide Electrolysis

A new technology, molten oxide electrolysis (MOE), aims to electrolyse molten iron ore into gaseous oxygen and the metal.[15] Clearly the process requires large quantities of electricity and can only be viable where there is easy access to cheap renewable energy, but it has the big advantage that no carbon dioxide is produced in the process. Research at MIT (Massachusetts Institute of Technology) aims to develop the process to a full industrial scale within two or three years and it is currently being commercialised by Boston Metal®. The system has the advantage of limiting the stages of production by using electrical energy directly to electrolyse the iron ore rather than using electricity to generate hydrogen which is then used to reduce the ore to sponge iron.

Low Temperature Electrolysis

ArcelorMittal[16] has announced that it will start the first industrial-scale low-temperature iron electrolysis plant in 2027. Initially the plant will produce about 60,000 tonnes per year, but this is anticipated to increase to between 300,000 and 1 million tonnes per year. The cold direct electrolysis process produces plates of steel from standard iron ore that can then be processed into steel in an electric arc furnace (EAF).

High Strength Steel

The new high strength steel S460M grade is designed for multi-storey high-rise buildings.[17] It offers the optimum balance between cost and weight with improved environmental performance. A reduction of 15% in mass is typical. High strength steels (HSS) are normally within the range of 420 to 700 MPa giving greater design flexibility. Typical uses are high-rise buildings, long-span roof trusses, bridges and steel-concrete composite units. The standards BS EN 10025[18] and BS EN10149[19,20] now refer to high strength steels with yield strengths up to 960 MPa. The use of high strength steels gives weight savings which are pro rata greater than the associated cost increases. Steels with yield strengths greater than 700 MPa are sometimes referred to as advanced high strength steels (AHSS).

S460 is 30% stronger than S355, but only 10–15% more expensive.

S690 is almost twice the strength of S355 but only about 30% more expensive.

Clearly the reduction in weight has environmental advantages with lower manufacturing and transportation CO_2 emissions also reduced building foundation requirements.

High strength steels are available as sheet, plate, sections, hollow sections, rods and bars. Delivered conditions for weldable high strength steels are normalized/normalized rolled (N), thermomechanical rolled (M) and quenched and tempered (Q). In order to obtain the higher strengths, HSS steels incorporate micro-alloying elements such as niobium (Nb) to cause the development of a finer grain structure and vanadium (V) or titanium (Ti) to enhance strength. High strength steel plates are now produced with yield strengths up to 1300 MPa. Weathering steels with improved corrosion resistance are produced in strengths up to S700.

The use of high strength steel can also lead to a reduction in the necessary fire protection such as a thinner layer of intumescent paint, although the use of thinner sections may permit a faster rise in temperature of the steel section.

Figure 13.1 Corten® weathering steel, Copenhagen. Photograph: Arthur Lyons

Weathering Steel

Weathering steel,[21] which contains small quantities of copper, usually between 0.25% and 0.55%, when exposed, forms a tenacious rust which prevents further corrosion and loss of material. It is estimated that exposed weathering steelwork can achieve a lifespan of up to 120 years with only minimal maintenance. It therefore has ecological advantages over standard grades of steel which, if exposed, will require regular maintenance. The use of weathering steel is therefore appropriate for exposed locations in buildings, bridges and other large structures, as illustrated by Figure 13.1.

Bio-Based Colour Coated Steel

The majority of standard colour coatings for steel such as PVC plastisol and polyvinylidene fluoride are based on petrochemical products. However, coatings based on vegetable oils are currently under development.[22] Vegetable oils can be converted into alkyd-based polyols, which are then reacted with diisocyanates to produce polyurethane coatings. The range of sources for the vegetable oils includes soybean, castor, cotton and rapeseed.

The Swedish SSAB Group has developed a bio-based coating, GreenCoat PLX®, which is manufactured with rapeseed oil. The product is available in a wide range of fast colours in either gloss or matt finish (Figure 13.2). As for traditional colour coatings, it is applied to 350 g/m^2 galvanized steel to a thickness of 36 μm. The reverse side has a nominal 12 μm coating. The material is manufactured to the standard BS EN 10169: 2022.[23]

Figure 13.2 GreenCoat® PLX coated steel. Coating manufactured from rapeseed oil. Photograph: Arthur Lyons

Fire Resistant Steel

Fire-resistant steel is normally considered to be steel that retains 67% of its room temperature strength at 600°C. This compares to conventional steel which retains only 47% of its room temperature strength at 600°C. Fire-resistant steel is manufactured in limited quantities as plate or rolled sections to a strength of 460 MPa.

Fire Resistance of Galvanized Steel

Research and testing have shown that steel galvanized to BS EN ISO 1461: 2022[24] has a greater fire resistance than non-galvanized steel of the same section.[25,26] Below 500°C the galvanized coating is stable and has a surface emissivity of approximately half that of a non-galvanized surface. This means that the rate at which the section heats up in fire is significantly reduced, giving greater fire protection, leading to an increased duration of fire resistance or load-bearing resistance to fire exposure for periods up to 30 minutes. The slower temperature rise is due solely to the reduced radiant heat flux entering the steel. Above 500°C the surface emissivity reverts to that of non-galvanized steel.

The use of galvanized steel may be advantageous in buildings such as single-storey residential / office and industrial structures that require fire resistance periods of 15 or 30 minutes, where the temperature of the steel members should only reach around 500°C. Additionally, the use of galvanized steel in single or multi-storey buildings, when combined with sprinklers, may enable a reduction of the minimum fire period to 30 minutes.

The new guidance on the fire resistance of galvanized steel sections will be in an amendment of the standard BS EN 1993-1-2[27] to be published around 2023.

Surface emissivity of non-galvanized steel ε_m= 0.070 for all temperatures

Surface emissivity of galvanized steel ε_m= 0.035 for θ_a < 500°C

Surface emissivity of galvanized steel ε_m= 0.070 for θ_a >500°C

3D-Printed Steel

Stainless steel can be 3D-printed using robotic technology. The system fabricates the required form from stainless steel rods held by a robotic unit equipped with welding gear. The system lends itself to the manufacture of small components but it is being geared up to the production of larger construction projects.

A 12-metre pedestrian bridge now installed over a canal in Amsterdam[28] (Figure 13.3) was manufactured using sophisticated robotic arms equipped with welding gear (Figure 13.4). The elegant structure in a curving S-form was 3D-printed from 4,500 kg of stainless steel and incorporates balustrades and lattice perforations designed using computer-modelling software. The complete bridge was then craned from the factory into position. The robotic technology offers the opportunity to use less material with the associated reduction in environmental impact. However, it is not anticipated that this new technology will replace conventional processes.[29]

Figure 13.3 3D-printed stainless steel bridge over the canal in Amsterdam. Photograph: Courtesy of MX3D and Thea den Heuvel

Aluminium Recycling

Production of primary aluminium is energy intensive both in the mining and smelting processes. One tonne of new aluminium produces 16.7t CO_2e. However, the metal is 100% recyclable without loss of structural integrity. Only 5% of the energy is required to recycle aluminium compared to virgin production from raw materials, so using 75% recycled material, one tonne of metal produces 2.3t CO_2e. However, only a third of the requirement for recycled aluminium can currently be met.

One difficulty with recycling aluminium is that various grades are used in construction for window frames, cladding, curtain walling and minor components. However, these can be identified using a spectrometer, prior to the disassembly of post-consumer products. The aim of the industry is to keep the grades separate to produce a true circular economy. If all aluminium is bunched together the resultant is a low-grade scrap, which is useable, but not for specialist purposes, such as grade 6063 (magnesium 7%, silicon 0.4%), which is used for window and door extrusions. The industry is therefore moving towards 'closed loop' recycling to maintain easy recyclability. Additionally, other materials such as polyamide and polyurethane need to be removed, but this is fully

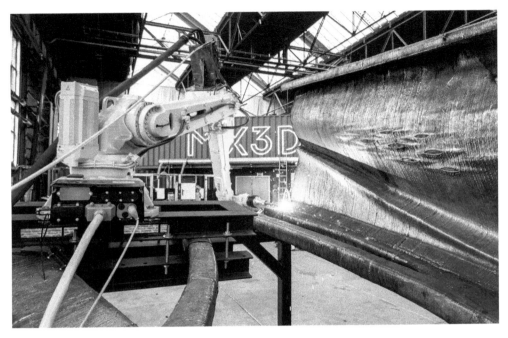

Figure 13.4 Manufacturing the Amsterdam bridge using 3D-stainless steel printing technology. Photograph: Courtesy of MX3D and Olivier de Gruijter

automated, and now chipped aluminium with minimal contaminants can be shipped back for smelting.

Aluminium Foam

Closed-cell aluminium foam is a lightweight insulating material consisting of up to 95% void space.[30] It is manufactured by injecting air into the aluminium melt to produce the foam which is then cooled. The incorporation of a fine dispersion of ceramic particles may be added to stabilise the air bubbles. Alternatively chemical blowing agents are incorporated in the aluminium melt. These reagents decompose to create bubbles producing a regular foam matrix.

Stabilised aluminium foam (SAF) is non-combustible and stiff, but of low density, hence its use in construction as thermal insulation. In addition, it has good sound-absorbing properties. Aluminium foam is fully recyclable and is usually formed from recycled material, but its production is energy-intensive.

Aluminium foam panels can be see-through if the outer layers on both faces are removed after forming. Alternatively, if the skin on the visible face only is removed from the foam, then deep cells are exposed. If both surfaces are unmodified after production, a delicate bubble surface is the visual feature. The lightweight panels (Figure 13.5) can be used for interior or exterior cladding and for a wide

Figure 13.5 Architectural use of Alusion® stabilised aluminium foam at Fondazione Prada, Milan, Italy. Photograph: Courtesy of Cymat Technologies Ltd.

range of interior design applications including lighting effects.

Copper Recycling

Copper recycling requires the separation of clean unalloyed metal from alloyed scrap. Pure copper can be directly reused, whereas contaminated copper requires purification by electrolysis. Recycling copper uses only 10% of the energy required to extract the metal from ore.

Antimicrobial Copper

Copper and copper alloys are naturally antimicrobial materials[31] and therefore have an important role in the reduction of hospital-acquired infections such as Covid-19, MRSA and E.*coli.* Providing that surfaces are cleaned regularly, copper kills 99% of germs within two hours of contact. As many infections are spread by touch, it is appropriate that touch surfaces such as door handles, push plates and hand rails within hospitals and other healthcare facilities should be manufactured from copper, brass or bronze rather than aluminium or stainless steel. Copper surfaces should not be lacquered or varnished as this reduces the antimicrobial efficacy.

Zinc Recycling

It is estimated that 60% of all zinc produced is still in use or reuse.[32] More than 25% of zinc currently in use has been previously recycled. Zinc sheet and die-cast parts are re-melted. Galvanized steel is re-melted by the steel industry, usually in an electric arc furnace (EAF). The zinc ends up as flue dust and 95% of this in North America and Europe is then concentrated and recycled. Zinc in brass is usually recycled by the copper industry into new brass.

References

1. *Sustainability performance of the steel industry 2003 – 2021*, World Steel Association – Sustainability Indicators 2022 Report, Brussels.
2. *Decarbonisation Action Report – Building Sustainable Futures*, Issue 1, 2023 (https://britishsteel.co.uk/media/409497/british-steel-decarbonisation-action-report-issue-1.pdf), British Steel Co. UK, Scunthorpe.
3. *World Steel in Figures 2022*, World Steel Association, Brussels.
4. *Model specification for the purchase of reclaimed steel sections*, March 2022, British Constructional Steelwork Association Ltd., London.
5. *Structural Steel Reuse – Assessment, Testing and Design Principles*, (SCI P427, 2019), Steel Construction Institute, Ascot. Update: *Reuse of pre-170 steelwork, Supplement to P427*, Brown, D.G. and Dougherty, L.A., (SCI P440, 2023), Steel Construction Institute, Ascot.
6. BES 6001: Framework Standard for Responsible Sourcing. v. 4.0, 2022, British Standards Institution, London.
7. British Standard BS EN ISO 14001: 2105. *Environmental management systems, Requirements with guidance for use.* BSI, London.
8. *Sustainability Specification for Structural Steelwork*, British Constructional Steelwork Association, 14 January 2022, London (Part of the National Steelwork Specification for Building Construction from 1 June 2022).
9. *Direct reduction of iron*, IIMA (https://www.metallics.org/dri-production.html), International Iron Metallics Association Ltd., Lewes, East Sussex.
10. *Powering a new, clean industrial revolution* (https://www.h2greensteel.com), H2GreenSteel, Boden, Sweden.
11. *Decarbonising Structural Steelwork*, CPD 01 2022, 11 February 2022, Building Magazine, London.
12. *ArcelorMittal makes first investment through its XCarb innovation fund,*

8 June 2021 (https://corporate. arcelormittal.com), ArcelorMittal, Luxembourg.

13. *ArcelorMittal inaugurates flagship carbon capture and utilisation project at its steel plant in Ghent, Belgium*, 8 December 2022 (https://corporate. arcelormittal.com/media/press-releases/arcelormittal.com), Arcelor-Mittal, Luxembourg.

14. *Sustainability Specification for Structural Steelwork*, British Constructional Steelwork Association, Annex J, London (Part of the National Steelwork Specification for Building Construction).

15. *Zero CO2 Steel by Molten Oxide Electrolysis. A Path to 100% Global Steel Decarbonisation* (bostonmetal.com/blog/), Boston Metal, Woburn, Massachusetts, USA.

16. *ArcelorMittal and John Cockerill announce plans to develop world's first industrial scale low temperature, iron electrolysis plant*, 14 June 2023, ArcelorMittal, Luxembourg.

17. *High Strength Steel Design and Execution Guide*, SCI (Steel Construction Institute), Steel Knowledge, Publication No. SCI P432, 2020, Ascot.

18. British Standard BS EN 10025-6 + A1: 2022. *Hot rolled products of structural steels. Technical delivery conditions for flat products of high yield strength structural steels in the quenched and tempered condition.* BSI, London.

19. British Standard BS EN 10149-1: 2013. *Hot rolled flat products made of high yield strength steels for cold forming. General technical delivery conditions.* BSI, London.

20. British Standard BS EN 10149-2: 2013. *Hot rolled flat products made of high yield steel for cold forming. Technical delivery conditions for thermomechanically rolled steel.* BSI, London.

21. British Standard BS EN 10025-5: 2019. *Hot rolled products of structural steels. Technical delivery conditions for structural steels with improved atmospheric corrosion resistance.* BSI, London.

22. *Bio-based polyurethane. An efficient and environment friendly coating systems. A review.* Progress in Organic Coatings. Vol. 91, pp. 25–32, 2016.

23. British Standard BS EN 10169: 2022. *Continuously organic coated (coil coated) steel flat products. Technical delivery conditions.* BSI, London.

24. British Standard BS EN ISO 1461: 2022. *Hot dipped galvanized coatings on fabricated iron and steel articles. Specifications and test methods.* BSI, London.

25. *New Steel Construction*, February 2021 p. 24 Meza, F., Steel Construction Institute, Ascot.

26. *Fire Resistance of Steel Sections Galvanized to EN ISO 1461: 2009*, SCI p. 429, 2020, Steel Construction Institute, Ascot.

27. British Standard BS EN 1993-1-2: 2005 Eurocode 3. (prBS EN 1993-1-2: 2022 Draft Eurocode 3) *Design of steel structures. Part 1-2 General rules – Structural fire design.* BSI, London.

28. *Joris Laarman's 3D-printed stainless steel bridge finally opens in Amsterdam*, Parkes, J., 19 July 2021, Dezeen, London.

29. *Challenges of building the world's first 3D printed steel bridge*, Kennedy, C., 7 December 2021, New Civil Engineer, London.

30. *Aluminium foam facades: Architecture rich in texture*, Franco, J.T., 6 May 2019, ArchDaily, New York.

31. *Antimicrobial touch surfaces*, (https://copper.org), Copper Development Association Inc., New York.

32. *Circular Economy – Recycling at All Costs? Zinc: Unleashing Valuable Resources* Grund, I.S., Van Genderen, E., Van Leeuwen, M., International Zinc Association, Proceedings of EMC 2019, Brussels, Research Gate, Berlin.

CHAPTER 14

Glass

CONTENTS

Introduction

The manufacture of float glass is highly energy intensive so the producers are investigating alternative fuels including biofuels and hydrogen. These systems are currently under development by the major manufacturers of glass products.

Standard float glass production and the wide range of decorative, fire protection, security, acoustic and solar control glasses including heat absorbing, heat reflecting, low-emissivity, multiple-glazing and laminates are well documented. Standard specialist glazing includes structural and one-way observation glass.

Recent innovations in glass and glazing are largely a response to the demand for greater thermal efficiencies of buildings which is reflected in changes to the Building Regulations. Glazing that generates electricity has great potential particularly for commercial buildings with large south-facing elevations. Specialist systems include electrically and thermally

DOI: 10.1201/9781003360469-14

switchable glazing, antimicrobial glass and self-cleaning glass.

Glass Manufacture

The current standard process for the manufacture of glass is energy intensive. A mixture of sand (silica) soda ash (sodium carbonate) and limestone (calcium carbonate) with small additions of salt cake (calcium sulphate) and dolomite (magnesian limestone) is heated in a furnace to 1600°C, with some broken glass (cullet). The molten mixture then flows across a shallow bath of molten tin at 1100°C contained in an atmosphere of hydrogen and nitrogen, which prevents oxidation of the surface, to produce the flat (float) glass. The temperature of the glass is gradually reduced until it solidifies at 600°C. The ribbon of glass is then trimmed and cut to standard lengths.

Pilkington® is currently researching alternative methods for heating the necessary furnaces to produce the melt. One alternative under investigation is the replacement of natural gas with hydrogen,[1] which would significantly reduce carbon emissions towards zero. An alternative interim measure under investigation is the use of a blend of natural gas and hydrogen as the furnace fuel. The latter alternative is under consideration as supplies of low-carbon hydrogen will be limited in the near future as the infrastructure to produce hydrogen by electrolysis and other processes using renewable energy will take time to be fully developed.

As soon as it is available, Pilkington aims to capitalise on the developing hydrogen supply network HyNet® in the North West of England and North Wales.[2] Low-carbon hydrogen is to be produced at the plant at Stanlow from natural gas and delivered through the developing extensive pipe network in the region. Hydrogen will be stored in the underground Nantwich salt mines to even out fluctuations in supply and demand. Initially, Pilkington's furnaces will use a 15% hydrogen/natural gas mix, but as the 100% hydrogen network is extended, the proportion of hydrogen used in the furnace mix will be increased. The HyNet pipe system will remove carbon dioxide for permanent disposal in the depleted oil and gas reservoirs under the seabed.

A further alternative to be researched by Kew Technology® and Pilkington® is the use of hydrogen-rich syngas (synthetic gas) produced from biomass and waste feedstocks. The CCH_2 (carbon capture and hydrogen) system, when operative will remove greenhouse gas while providing hydrogen-rich fuel to fire up the glass production furnaces.

A different approach to decarbonising glass production involves the use of biofuels to fire the furnaces.[3] The biofuel used in the initial experimentation by Pilkington was made from organic waste and it emits around 60% less CO_2 than the traditional natural gas used. In the first trial the float line furnace was fired with biofuel for four days to produce 165,000 m^2 of the usual high-quality product. It is considered that biofuels offer a realistic transitory manufacturing process before truly zero-carbon glass, either hydrogen or electrically produced, is commercially practical.

Building Regulations

Under the Building Regulations Approved Document Part L, Conservation of Fuel and Power 2021 edition – England,[4] the notional target for windows and glazed doors in new buildings has been reduced to 1.2 W/m²K. The limiting values, which are the maximum U-values permitted, are now set at 1.6 W/m²K. It is likely that the next revision of the Approved Document Part L in 2025 will further reduce the target U-value for windows to 0.8 W/m²K when it is expected that the Future Homes Standard will require all new homes to be zero-carbon ready.

The Building Regulations Part O, Overheating – England,[5] require systems to mitigate the effects of overheating in buildings. The regulation applies to new residential buildings only. It requires the limitation of unwanted solar gain in summer, the means to remove unwanted excessive heat which should be done by passive means rather than mechanical ventilation if at all possible.

Multiple Glazing

As the Future Homes Standard[6] anticipated for 2025 approaches, the majority of the double glazing industry is targeting a standard window U-value of 0.8 W/m²K. This can be achieved with vacuum or krypton-filled timber-frame double-glazed units. However, the industry is anticipating that in the long term triple glazing is likely to be the general solution for energy efficiency. Aluminium triple-glazed units incorporating Aerogel® within the thermal break achieve a U-value of 0.8 W/m²K and a U-value as low as 0.72 W/m²K can be reached within a 70 mm thick aluminium frame system. Similarly, a 76mm thick PVC-U

frame system can achieve a U-value of 0.73 W/m²K. One PVC-U manufacturer has already produced a quadruple glazing system with a U-value of 0.5 W/m²K and a Window Energy Rating (WER) of A+40 in anticipation of even tighter standards. A 120 mm solid aluminium reinforced PVC-U door can achieve a U-value of 0.51 W/m²K and where required may incorporate 78 mm quadruple glazing without significant loss of thermal performance.[7] The performance requirements for windows and doors are detailed in British Standard BS 6375: Parts 1–3[8] and PAS 24: 2022.[9]

Solar Control Glass

Solar control glasses modify the transmittance of light and heat compared to standard clear float glass. The energy flow is controlled by a balanced combination of absorptance, reflectance and transmittance within the outer layer of a multi-layer insulating glass unit (IGU) (Figure 14.1). The proportion of light and solar radiant heat transmitted is specified by a two-digit manufacturers' coding. For example, Pilkington® Suncool® 70/35[10] gives 70% light transmittance and 35% heat transmittance. Solar control glasses are typically grey, green, blue, bronze or silver. Solar control glasses may be combined with other specialist glazing systems within IGUs.[11]

Low Emissivity Glass

Over 25% of heat from public buildings is lost through the glazing. This can be

converted into electricity.[14] Currently the efficiency of conversion is low compared to standard solar panels, but glass remains transparent to visible light. The systems have great potential for generating power on buildings with large glazed façades. The ultra-thin laminates are typically manufactured from thin-film silicon, perovskites or organic photovoltaic compounds. The coating manufactured by SolarWindow Technologies®[15] which is available in a range of colours and transparencies, can be applied to glass, plastic and other surfaces. It is effective on all building elevations.

One laminated glass system[16] (Polysolar®) uses thin-film cadmium-telluride (CdTe) photovoltaic technology to produce a glazing unit which generates electricity with optical transmission within the range 80% to opaque. The glazing units have a range of appearance from colourless through grey to pixelated black. Coloured laminates are also

available. Electrical generation efficiency is around 12% or 118 W/m^2 and standard panels are 1200 mm × 600 mm × 7.1 mm. Semi-transparent systems use black mono-crystalline silicon (c-Si) photovoltaic technology which gives greater electrical generation at 20% or 210 W/m^2 efficiency but with reduced (10%) light transmission. The glazing units are constructed of a series of laminates with the photovoltaic layer sandwiched between conductive electrode laminates which connect to the wiring hidden within the glazing surround. The electricity generated is then fed via an inverter into the building's power supply or to the national grid as appropriate.

A quite different system[17] (ClearVue®) separates visible light from the ultraviolet and infrared rays before turning the latter into electricity (Figure 14.3). The majority of the visible light passes unaffected through the glazing system. The glazing units comprise a four-layer system with a

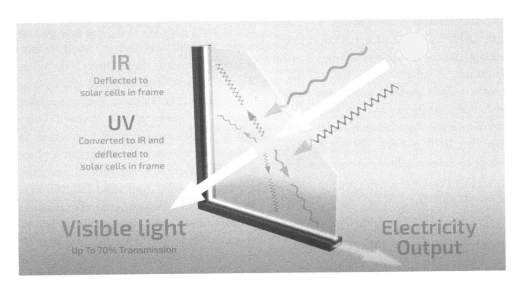

Figure 14.3 Electricity generating glass. Diagram: Courtesy of ClearVuePV®, Perth, West Australia

central inorganic PVB layer. Incident solar radiation is separated into visible light and UV/IR rays by a spectrally selective film. Up to 70% of the visible light passes straight through. The UV is converted into IR, and 90% of the non-visible rays are bounced back into the inorganic PVB layer. The IR rays are then scattered by the nanoparticles in the interlayer to the edges of the glass panel where hidden solar cells convert the radiation into electrical energy. The ClearVue system can be integrated with any other glazing functionality such as blinds, shutters surveillance cameras and automatic tinting. Remote control using artificial intelligence (AI) systems gives functionality from smartphones. The multilayer system has good insulating properties.

Building-integrated photovoltaic (BIPV) modules[18] can be incorporated into buildings as an alternative to conventional construction materials not only for glazing but also for façades, roofs, rain screens, sound insulating screens and skylights. They are particularly appropriate for tall commercial buildings where the energy savings can be significant. A major advantage of BIPV systems is that they form an integral part of the building envelope and are not bolt-on units which can have adverse visual effects. Thin film BIPV systems are usually based on copper/indium/gallium/selenium (CIGS) or copper/indium/selenium (CIS) photovoltaic technology.

Thermochromic Glass

Thermochromic photovoltaic glazing[19] can generate electricity and will automatically change colour when heated to enhance shading, reduce glare and block excessive solar gain. The twofold gain is a reduction in the requirement for air conditioning and the generation of electricity. The system is based on a thin film of perovskite, sandwiched between two panes of glass and with solvent vapour injected into the gap. When the temperature rises to 35–45°C the encapsulated vapour changes the normally transparent perovskite crystals to rearrange them into different shapes (chain, sheet and cube) changing the colour from yellow, orange, red and brown thus reducing excessive solar gain.

Perovskites are organometallic compounds, such as methyl ammonium lead halide (bromide or iodide), that have a good generating efficiency compared to standard silicon solar cells. Research in this area is continuing in the US.

Water-Filled Glass

Water-filled glass (WFG)[20] is a new glazing system in which a layer of water is embedded between the sheets of glass (Figure 14.4). It changes façade glazing into a solar panel. In summer the water layer absorbs heat reducing the internal overheating. The excess heat is transferred to thermal storage such as underground pipework. In winter the constant temperature underground water is recycled into the glass laminate, maintaining a steady temperature throughout the year, thus reducing winter heat loss through cold glazing. An alternative system uses a heat pump to maintain the water in the glass at an appropriate temperature. The system is ideally suited to

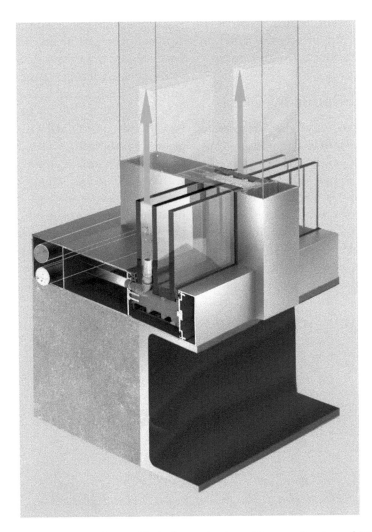

Figure 14.4 Isometric diagram of water-filled glass technology. Diagram: Courtesy of WFG®

south-oriented glazing or appropriate roof lights and can save energy compared to the equivalent standard double or triple glazing. Alternatively, the system can be a retrofit on existing buildings to improve internal thermal comfort. In cases where overheating exists in one space, the excess heat can be transferred to other areas where heating is required, thus saving on energy use.

Bendable Glass

Ultra-thin bendable Willow® glass[21] manufactured by Corning® to thicknesses of 100 and 200 microns is available in 1.3 m rolls of up to 300 m in length. The scratch-resistant and easy-to-clean material can be bent on site and laminated to other substrates to produce a clean shiny surface. The fusion-formed material is virtually free of any defects and offers an alternative to traditional flat glass sheets.

Bird-Impact-Reducing Glass

Avisafe® is an innovative glass designed to reduce the number of bird impacts on glass façades.[22] The striped pattern on the outside of the external leaf of an Insulating Glass Unit (IGU) is visible to birds in the UV part of the spectrum and disrupts the reflections of sky and surroundings which otherwise would be seen (Figures 14.5 and 14.6). Birds can clearly see the bright glass stripes rather than just reflections of the sky and surroundings, and therefore realise that something is there. The pattern is barely visible from the inside. This special bird-impact-reducing glass is available annealed or toughened in thicknesses from 4 to 10 mm and sizes up to 6000 × 3210 mm. It can be combined with other special glasses for thermal insulation, solar control, noise control or safety and security within standard Insulating Glass Units.

An alternative system involves the printing of dots or geometric shapes onto the glass surface using laser print technology. The treatment is applied on the outside of the exterior pane to reduce the mirroring effect of adjacent trees and

Figure 14.5 Pilkington Avisafe® bird-impact-reducing glass – exterior view. Photograph: Courtesy of Pilkington UK

Figure 14.6 Pilkington Avisafe® bird-impact-reducing glass – interior view. Photograph: Courtesy of Pilkington UK

planting. It prevents bird collisions in the same way as the Avisafe system.

Anti-reflective Glass

Anti-reflective glass reduces the surface reflection associated with standard float glass to less than 2%, giving virtually un-obscured reflection-free vision. The material is available as single sheet with the coating on one surface or as a PVB laminate with the coating on both outer faces.

Anti-condensation Glass

Anti-condensation glass has a low-emissivity coating on the external face of the outer pane within an insulating glass unit (IGU). Anti-condensation glass can be laminated, toughened, bent or combined with any other functional glasses within IGUs. As the low-emissivity coating is external, units incorporating anti-condensation glass require careful handling on site. Light transmittance within a triple-glazed unit is up to 68%.

Antimicrobial Glass

SaniTise® is an on-line coated glass with a photocatalytic coating providing antimicrobial properties.[23] It protects against the transmission of viruses on frequently touched surfaces which have access to UV radiation from either natural daylight or other sources. The on-line coating works in two stages. Firstly, the coating reacts with atmospheric water in a photocatalytic process to produce reactive oxygen species. Subsequently, the reactive species provide antimicrobial properties by breaking down the enveloped viruses on the glass surface. Antimicrobial glass can reduce the risk virus transmission on surfaces like doors and windows, particularly in high-risk settings such as hospitals, medical surgeries, care homes and schools.

Self-Cleaning Glass

Self-cleaning glass[24] has a 15 μm invisible hard coating which incorporates two features. The surface containing titanium dioxide (TiO_2) is photocatalytic absorbing ultraviolet light, which, with oxygen from the air, breaks down or loosens organic material on the glass surface. The surface is also hydrophilic, causing rainwater to spread evenly over the surface rather than running down as droplets. This ensures that any surface residues are washed away without forming unsightly streaks. Self-cleaning glass has a faint blue tint and a slightly greater mirror effect than standard float glass. It is available as standard annealed glass as well as toughened or laminated. Self-cleaning glass is effective down to pitches of 10° and can be incorporated into Insulating Glass Units (IGUs) with other specialist glasses.

Infrared Heating Panels

Pilkington® has developed infrared radiator panels[25] manufactured from electrically conductive glass which converts electrical energy into heat. The slim-line panels are available in standard polar white or mirror glass which is suitable for installation in humid atmospheres such as bathrooms. The panels, which are available in a range of sizes and power ratings, are designed to operate with intelligent building control systems and sophisticated building management systems.

LED Edge-Lit Glass

LED edge-lit glass allows custom-etched designs to be illuminated. The system uses low-iron ultra-white toughened glass with LED lights at the perimeter to illuminate the pattern. The etched pattern is illuminated to any colour and can be programmed to change on demand. The track system of illumination allows the units to act as sliding doors. Edge-lit glass can also be used creatively for illuminating sculptures. The typical maximum unit size is 4 m × 1.5 m.

Recycling Glass

Glass from old double- and single-glazing units can be crushed and used as high-quality cullet in the manufacture of new float glass reducing the requirement for virgin sand. Every tonne of recycled cullet saves approximately 300 kg of CO_2 emissions. Recycling organisations channel off the other materials such as spacer bars to separate waste streams.

Bottle and other glass is being recycled into glass ceramics by Glaskeramik® in Germany.[26] The material produced can be 100% recycled again at its end-of-life. Reclaimed glass is recycled into large clear or coloured panels up to 2800 × 1250 mm. The production process involves the classification, including colour sorting, followed by crushing of the reclaimed glass which is then shaped into panels and sintered. The sintered product is then cooled under controlled conditions, polished if required and cut to the required dimensions. Colours include black and brown, through blue and green to white and clear. Additional effects can be created by blending in contrasting coloured granules. Finishes are natural, polished or matt and thicknesses are in the range of 12 mm to 20 mm.

As the starting material is recycled glass and the product can be recycled again, the production process can be considered as an example of a Cradle-to-Cradle circular system. Glaskeramik® is rated by the RICS (Royal Institution of Chartered Surveyors)

as an environmentally friendly and sustainable material.

Aluminium Oxynitride

Aluminium oxynitride[27] (ALON®) is a transparent material which is much more durable than standard glass. The sheet material is manufactured from white aluminium oxynitride powder, which is pressed under extreme pressure at 2000°C to produce the solid material, which is then ground and polished to give clear see-through surfaces. The material is transparent in the UV and medium IR regions of the electromagnetic spectrum. ALON is four times harder than fused standard silica glass, and can therefore be used for high-security / bullet-proof windows. The current maximum window size is 450 × 900 mm.

References

1. *Architectural glass powered by hydrogen in world first*, 30 August 2021 (https://www.pilkington.com/en-gb/uk/news-highlights/latest/architectural-glass-production-powered-by-hydrogen-in-world-first), Pilkington, Lancashire.
2. *Unlocking a low carbon future* (https://hynet.co.uk), HyNet, North West.
3. *Biofuel trial by St Helens glass giant marks new world-first towards decarbonisation*, 28 February 2022, Pilkington, St Helens.
4. Building Regulations (England): Approved Document L, Conservation of fuel and power:

Volume 1: Dwellings, 2021 edition incorporating 2023 amendments.
Volume 2: Buildings other than Dwellings, 2021 edition incorporating 2023 amendments.

5. Building Regulations (England) Approved Document O, Overheating, 2021, updated 2022.

6. Future Homes Standard. Department for Levelling Up, Housing and Communities and Ministry of Housing & Local Government. To be published in 2025.

7. Glass Times, pp. 46, 52 and 84, Vol. 17, Issue 6, June 2023, Times Publishing Ltd., Manchester.

8. British Standard BS 6375. *Performance of windows and doors*:
Part 1: 2015 + A1: 2016: *Classification for weathertightness and guidance on selection and specification.*
Part 2: 2009: *Classification for operation and strength characteristics and guidance on selection and specification.*
Part 3: 2009 + A1: 2013: *Classification for additional performance characteristics and guidance on selection and specification.* BSI, London.

9. British Standard PAS 24: 2022: *Enhanced security performance requirements for doorsets and windows in the UK.* BSI, London.

10. *Pilkington Suncool 70/35 – Solar control glazing suitable for new build and all aspects of the modern home*, June 2021, Pilkington UK Ltd., NSG Group, Lancashire.

11. British Standard BS EN 1096-1: 2012. *Glass in Building – Coated Glass. Definitions and Classification.* BSI, London.

12. *Smart glass opens a window to new applications*, Radiant Vision Systems (https://www.radiantvisionsystems.com/blog/smart-glass-opens-window-new-application), 7 March 2022, Redmond, Washington, USA.

13. *Curved switchable smart glass* (https://intelligentglass.net/products/curved-switchable-smart-glass/), 5 December 2020, Intelligent Glass, Hoyland, South Yorkshire.

14. *Solar windows: The future of sustainable building and design*, 1 August 2023 (https://www.futurebuild.co.uk), Future Build News.

15. *Electricty-generating liquid coatings and processes* (https://www.solarwindow.com/technology/), SolarWindow Technologies Inc., New York.

16. *Polysolar Energy, product specifications and datasheets* (https://polysolar.com/energy_info/specifications), Polysolar Energy, London.

17. *Say bonjour to solar glass by ClearVue* (https://clearvuepv.com), ClearVue Technologies Ltd., Perth, Australia.

18. *Transparent solar photovoltaic glazing (BIPV)* (https://ukgbc.org/resources/transparent-solar-photovoltaic-glazing-bipv), UK Green Building Council, London.

19. *Thermochromic photovoltaic windows*, Tech Briefs – Engineering Solutions for Design & Manufacturing, 22 December 2021, New York.

20. *Water-filled windows use sunlight to heat and cool buildings*, Barker, Nat., 3 January 2023, Dezeen, London.

21. *Corning Willow Glass* (https://www.corning.com/emea/en/innovation/corning-emerging-innovations/

corning-willow-glass,html), Corning, Arizona, USA.

22. *Pilkington Avisafe – Glass designed to protect birds* (https://www.pilkington. com/en-gb/uk/products/product-categories/special-applications/pilkin gton-avisafe), Pilkington, Lancashire.

23. *Pilkington SaniTise antimicrobial glass* (https://www.pilkington.com/en-gb/ uk/products/product-categories/ health-applications/pilkington-sanitise), Pilkington, Lancashire.

24. *Pilkington Activ self-cleaning glass* (https://www.pilkington.com/en-gb/ uk/householders/types-of-glass/self-cleaning-glass), Pilkington, Lancashire.

25. *Pilkington debuts sustainable infrared heating solution*, Morris, G., 6 March 2023, Glass International, Quartz Business Media Ltd., Redhill, Surrey.

26. *Our crystallized Glaskeramik is sustainable thanks to 100% upcycled glass* (https://www.magna-glaskeramik. com), Magna Glaskeramik, Germany.

27. *Aluminium oxynitride*, Crouch, I.G., in 'The Science of Armour Materials', 2017, Imprint of Woodhead Publishing, Elsevier, Amsterdam.

CHAPTER 15

Stone and Ceramics

CONTENTS

Introduction

There are just a modest number of innovations in relation to stone and ceramic building materials. In the context of energy conservation, the developments of photovoltaic slates and tiles which merge into the traditional materials are of positive benefit where major roof installations would otherwise have a negative visual effect. New rock-based cladding panels have the significant advantage in the post-Grenfell era of offering the maximum fire rating.

Low Pitch Slate and Tile Roofing

Innovations by Permavent® enable slate and plain tile roofs to be built to significantly lower pitches than was previously possible.[1] The slate system (Figure 15.1) involves the inclusion of a PVC insert which cushions the slate to prevent rattling and ensures a sealed gap between adjacent slates. If used in combination with the appropriate breather membrane, slates can be built to a pitch as low as 12°. The system ensures that the battens remain dry enhancing the durability of the roof system. The PVC inserts are available in lengths of 400, 500 and 600 mm to fit reclaimed or new slates.

The system for plain tiles similarly ensures that any moisture penetrating between adjacent tiles is shed down the roof, keeping the structure dry, and it especially prevents the ingress of wind-driven rain. The system can be used for

DOI: 10.1201/9781003360469-15

Figure 15.1 Permavent® slates with a PVC insert enabling a minimum pitch of 12° to be constructed. Photograph: Arthur Lyons

standard machine-made plain tiles which would normally be limited to a minimum pitch of 35°. When used with the appropriate breather membrane a minimum pitch of 17.5° is achievable. The units for plain tiles are supplied to a length of 1237 mm.

Photovoltaic Slates and Tiles

Photovoltaic roofing slates (Figure 15.2) which have the appearance of natural slate roofing are made from aluminium and glass.[2] They can be used adjacent to real slates or made into a complete edge-to-edge

solar roof. Individual PV slates 500 × 250 mm have a peak output of 28 W. The slates have a minimum pitch of 22.5° and are light grey in colour. Standard sizes are 600 × 300 mm, 500 × 300 mm and 500 × 250 mm.

Concrete or clay photovoltaic tiles in charcoal or terracotta can fill up to 98% of the area of a pitched roof and match standard tiles of the same colour, preventing spoiling the overall aesthetic of a pitched roof with large glazed PV units. Standard tiles are 298 × 342 mm which produce a peak output of 15 W per unit, but will operate in low light conditions.

Figure 15.2 Photovoltaic slates which match and coordinate with standard roofing slates. Photograph: Arthur Lyons

Rockpanels

Rockpanels® (Figure 15.3) are durable cladding panels manufactured from naturally occurring basalt volcanic rock with an organic or inorganic coating.[3] The panels, typically 6, 8 or 9 mm thick are available in a wide variety of finishes including smooth, natural, metallic effect and wood effect. Colours are matt, silk or high gloss which can be to RAL[4] or NCS[5] codes if required. The finish is a water-based coating which gives UV protection with self-cleaning as an option. The boards can be curved and worked with standard tools, also routed or cut to produce three-dimensional effects. The fire rating is B-s2,d0 for the standard board, but A2-s1,d0 is available to comply with the latest Building Regulations[6,7] for medium and high-rise buildings. The natural rock material is fully recyclable into new rock panels. Standard sizes are 1200 or 1250 × 2500 or 3000 mm. The thermal conductivity of the standard 8 mm board is $\lambda = 0.37$ W/mK, and for the 9 mm board $\lambda = 0.55$ W/mK.

Natural Stone Roll

Marmox® natural stone as a mosaic, is now produced as a 4 mm thick roll of material,

Figure 15.3 A selection of Rockpanels®, durable cladding panels, illustrating the range of colours and textures. Photograph: Arthur Lyons

with an inbuilt waterproof layer. The Indian sedimentary stone, treated with clear polycarbonate is waterproof, stain and UV resistant. The mosaic is available in a range of beige, brown and grey multicolours and a selection of finishes (Figure 15.4). The mosaic tile units are available in sizes 2.5 and 5 mm square with a 3 mm spacing for grout. The standard roll size is 1000 × 500 mm, and the stock sheet size is 300 × 300 mm. The material is suitable for bathrooms and similar wet room spaces.

Marmox® thin stone sheets are also available as 4 ± 1.5 mm veneer sheets.[8] The sedimentary stone is backed with a

Figure 15.4 Marmox® Indian sedimentary stone illustrating a range of textures. Photograph: Arthur Lyons

stabilising fleece and the surface is treated with polycarbonate to produce a water-proof and stain-resistant surface for easy removal of excess grout. Standard sheet sizes are 1200 × 610 mm, 2100 × 1050 mm and 2400 × 1050 mm. The sheet material is suitable for both internal and external use, and can be curved if required.

Flexible Ceramic Textile

Ceramic textile[9] is a flexible material composed of a steel wire mesh enclosed in a matrix of ceramic clay tiles stacked in horizontal or vertical bands. The material, Flexbrick®, can be folded to mould into any curved form and is suitable for covering walls, floors and façades creating the effect of a structure wrapped in a terracotta blanket. The material is manufactured in lengths up to 20 m. The steel wires hold the individual ceramic pieces through slots or perforations at both ends. Void spaces can be incorporated into the design to create sunscreens. Fixing requires a steel support system similar to curtain hanging. The material can be recycled as it only uses steel mesh and ceramic elements which are easily separated.

Terrazzo

Terrazzo floors and tiles are traditionally made with crushed natural stone (usually marble or granite) in polished concrete or two-part epoxy resin. However, it is possible to create terrazzo with many recycled materials such as broken glass, reclaimed ceramic materials or metal (brass, aluminium or zinc) offcuts. Terrazzo floors are durable and appropriate for high-foot traffic areas such as schools, airports and sports arenas.

Sensitiles

Sensitiles (Figure 15.5) are concrete, resin, glass or terrazzo tiles which incorporate light-transmitting acrylic fibres.[10] The acrylic fibres act as light pipes by absorbing light which then emerges at the other end of the fibre. By incorporating these fibres randomly into a solid matrix, the surface responds to shadow movement, touch, varying light and changing colours producing a twinkling and scattering effect. Sensitile® manufactures a wide range of products including some

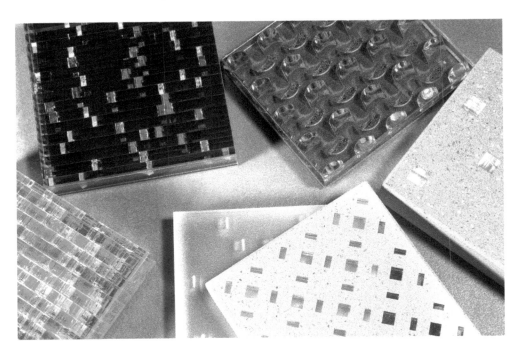

Figure 15.5 Sensitile® light-transmitting tiles. Photograph: Courtesy of Sensitile Inc.

which are further activated by hidden LED light sources. The light-sensitive products can be used for room dividers, floors, work surfaces and within water features.

References

1. *Permavent innovative roofing solutions* (https://www.permavent.co.uk/products/easy-slate), Permavent, Weymouth, Dorset.
2. *Photovoltaic slates* (https://www.gb-sol.co.uk/products/pvslates/default.htm), GB-Sol, Cardiff.
3. *Rockpanel colours* (https://www.rockpanel.co.uk/products-overview/rockpanel-colours/), Rockwool Ltd., Bridgend.
4. RAL – The colour system developed in Germany in 1925 now with 210 standard colours which are defined by a four-digit code and an auxiliary colour shade description.
5. NCS – The Natural Color System® developed in Sweden, defines all colours scientifically with a specific alpha-numeric reference code.
6. Fire safety and high-rise residential buildings (from 1 August 2021) – England. UK Government – Department for Levelling up, Housing & Communities and Ministry of Housing, communities and Local Government, 24 June 2021.
7. Building Regulations, Approved Document (fire safety) Volume 1: Dwellings and Volume 2: Buildings other than dwellings. UK Government. 2019 edition with 2022 amendments for use in England.
8. *Natural stone finish in large format, ultra-thin sliced stone sheets* (https://marmox.co.uk/products/slicedstone-veneer-sheets), Marmox UK Ltd., Chatham, Kent.
9. *Algorithm-based architecture: Flexible bricks to wrap architectural spaces* (https://archdaily.com), Tovar, E., 26 July 2023, Arch Daily, Zurich, Switzerland.
10. *Sensitiles* (https://www.sensitile.com), Sensitile Inc., Ypsilanti, Michigan, USA.

CHAPTER 16

Plastics

CONTENTS

Introduction

Traditional plastic materials are derived mainly from petrochemicals and their manufacture accounts for approximately 2% of the world's carbon emissions. The industry is aware that decarbonising will require major capital expenditure and increased sales costs in order to reach net zero by 2050. Professional estimates[1] predict that the demand for polypropylene, polyethylene and polyethylene terephthalate (PET) will nearly double by 2050. However, recycling is set to ameliorate the situation as it is estimated that 35% of the plastics demand by 2050 could be met by bioplastics and recycled material. Indeed, if there is a greater acceleration in recycling, a drop in the consumption of single-use plastics and an enhanced use of bio-based manufacturing feedstocks, then the peak demand of oil for plastic production may be reached in 2043 followed by a gradual decline to 2050.

Bioplastics

Bioplastics[2] can be manufactured from a wide range of renewable biomass materials such as vegetable fats and oils, corn starch, sugar cane, recycled food waste, recycled cellulose, timber waste, algae and marine chitins. They have the advantage over conventional fossil-fuel plastics that they degrade more readily when discarded, although some CO_2 is produced in the

DOI: 10.1201/9781003360469-16

process. Bioplastics have the potential to be used in structural elements and cladding – subject to appropriate fire regulations.

One new bioplastic material, manufactured by Made-of-Air® in Berlin, is formed from biochar[3] (see also Chapter 11 – Insulation Materials page 202). Biochar is mixed with a binder from sugar cane making it into a mouldable bioplastic containing 90% carbon. The material can be used for building façades, interiors and urban infrastructure. At end-of-life the bioplastic can be ground up and returned to the earth. Currently, bioplastics are more expensive than conventional materials.

3D Printed Plastics

The Dutch firm Aectual® is using large 3D printers to create complex structures from recycled and renewable plant-based polymers.[4] The material is fully recyclable and any errors can be recovered by shredding the material and returning it to the mix. The plastic is eminently suitable for the production of architectural and interior products such as internal decorative screens, wall panels and sunshades, also larger units including stairs and façades.

Recycled PVC

End-of-life PVCu window and door frames and virgin offcuts are increasingly being recycled to be reused in the fabrication of new fenestration products. New processing techniques enable 55% of the reprocessed material to be extruded into new sections. Coloured PVC has to be re-purposed for other outlets such as rainwater goods. According to the BRE[5] (Building Research Establishment), PVC products can be recycled up to 10 times without impact on performance and can have a service life of at least 35 years. Metal waste must be separated out and recycled appropriately.

The multi-stage process for recycling PVCu involves the shredding of the material into 60 mm particles, the removal of foreign particles and then further grinding to 10 mm. Electrostatic and optical sorting remove unwanted and coloured material leaving the PVCu ready for re-extrusion into new sections. The latest technology[6] produces recycled PVCu with purities of 99.5% in one pass. The process radically changes the sustainability of PVCu within building construction, as it significantly reduces the quantity of material deposited in landfill sites, making the material part of the circular economy.

Since 2000, the European PVC industry has recycled 6.5 million tonnes of PVC into new products, preventing the release of 13 million tonnes of CO_2 into the atmosphere. In 2021 0.8 million tonnes of PVC was recycled.[7] In addition, manufacturers have significantly reduced the energy required to produce PVC resin and fabricated products.

Recycled Mixed Plastics

Many plastics can be recycled, but general plastic waste which is a mixture of products requires sorting into individual plastic types, such as polystyrene, polycarbonate, etc. The individual plastic material can then be shredded or flaked into recycled pellets for melting and reforming into panels. The panels produced have a range of colours with graining associated with the variable feedstock, giving the appearance of terrazzo or marble stone.

The material is available in 800 × 800 mm sheets with the options of added fire resistance or UV protection. The material can be cut, plastic welded, routed or laser etched. Uses include wall cladding and a wide range of minor components such as signage, work surfaces and furniture. Recycling plastic packaging waste converts a short-life product into a durable material reducing landfill and general waste pollution.

Resin-Bound Permeable Paving

Permeable surfaces permit the natural drainage of rainwater to reduce the risk of storm flooding. The Addagrip® system[8] (Figure 16.1) combines a resin-bonded, SuDS (Sustainable Drainage Systems) compliant, porous surface of natural or recycled aggregates with a system of buried

Figure 16.1 Resin bonded Sustainable Drainage System (SuDS) (Addagrip®), using natural or recycled aggregate. Photograph: Arthur Lyons

pipework. The surface can be heated in the winter from grey waste water to prevent freezing or to melt lying snow. In the summer period the heating of the resin surface can be harnessed through a heat pump to provide hot water. The permeable surface prevents the build-up of surface water.

Anti-seismic Thermoplastic Carbon Fibre Composite

Cabkoma® is a carbon fibre strand rod coated with an outer layer of inorganic fibre impregnated with thermoplastic resin.[9] The material has high tensile strength, good durability and weighs about $^1/_5$ that of steel. The material, developed in Japan, is used for retrofit earthquake protection on buildings which were not designed to cope with severe seismic forces. The strands when attached appropriately to the building framework and earth fixings will transmit earthquake forces directly to the ground, reducing vibrations which otherwise could cause catastrophic damage or collapse. The strands are manufactured to 7.0, 8.2 and 9.3 mm diameter in 160 m rolls. The material is also manufactured in sheet form composed of carbon fibre impregnated with thermoplastic epoxy resin. Typically, it can be wrapped around corroded steel columns to give a medium-term repair.

2-Dimensional Polymer

Engineers at the Massachusetts Institute of Technology (MIT) have created a totally new type of polymeric material which has great potential for the construction industry.[10] The new polymer is a two-dimensional

polyaramide to which they have designated the term 2DPA-1. This material contrasts with all standard polymers which are an agglomeration of linear polymer chains. The flat two-dimensional molecular structure gives the material great strength as it eliminates the gaps that exist between adjacent linear polymer chains at the molecular level. The material has twice the strength of a typical steel, with a yield strength of 488 MPa compared to e.g. 250 MPa, but with only $^1/_6$ of the density. Because of its molecular structure, the material is highly impermeable which gives it the potential to act as a protective layer over less durable materials such as steel.

The plastic is manufactured at room temperature from standard starting materials to produce initially a powder. This is then dissolved in trifluoroacetic acid and spun on a flat substrate to form a nanofilm. In principle, the nanofilms could be stacked to produce a building material or made into fibres for uses similar to those currently for carbon fibres. It is anticipated that the material should be recyclable rather than dumped into landfill sites.

3-Dimensional Graphene

Scientists at Massachusetts Institute of Technology (MIT)[11,12] are investigating the potential applications for 3D Graphene. The material has a density which is only 5% that of steel, but it is stiff and strong with ten times the strength. It therefore has potential uses within construction as a structural or insulating material, but research and development is still in the early stages.

References

1. *The world's addiction to plastics in five charts*, Bloomberg NEF, 16 August 2022 (https://about.brief.com/blog/the-worlds-addiction-to-plastic-in-five-charts/). New York.

2. *Bioplastics for a circular economy* Rosenboom, J-G., Langer, R. and Traverso, G., Nature Reviews Materials, Vol. 7, pp. 117–137, 2022, Springer Nature Ltd., Berlin.

3. *Atmospheric CO_2 is our biggest resource says carbon-negative plastic brand Made-of-Air*, Hahn, J., 24 June 2021, Dezeen, London.

4. *Truly circular interior objects and architectural systems* (https://www.aectual.com), Aectual, Amsterdam.

5. *The Green Guide to Specification*, 4th edition, BRE Global, Anderson, J., Shiers, D. and Steele, K., 2009, Wiley-Blackwell, Chichester.

6. *CNC Recycling invests £2m in state-of-the-art facility*, Glass Times, March 2023.

7. *Progress report 2022 – Reporting on 2021 activities*, Vinyl Plus – committed to sustainable developments, p. 31, Brussels.

8. *Resin bound and bonded surfacing* (https://addagrip.co.uk), Addagrip Terraco Ltd., Uckfield.

9. *Thermoplastic carbon fibre composite* (https://www.komatsumatere.co.jp/cabkoma/en/), Komatsumatere Co. Ltd., Japan.

10. *Irreversible synthesis of an ultrastrong two-dimensional polymeric material*, Zeng, Y., Gordiichuk, P., Ichihara, T., Zhang, G. et al., Nature, 2 February 2022, Vol. 602, pp. 91–95, Springer Nature, London.

11. *The mechanism and design of a lightweight three-dimensional graphene assembly*, Qin, Z., Jung, G.S., Kan, M.J. and Buehler, M., 6 January 2017, Vol. 3, Issue 1, Science Advances, Washington.

12. *New 3D graphene is ten times as strong as steel*, Szondy, D., 9 January 2017, New Atlas, Gizmag Pty. Ltd., Victoria, Australia.

CHAPTER 17

Plaster

CONTENTS

Introduction

Clay and lime plasters offer an alternative to the standard gypsum plaster which is manufactured by heating gypsum within the range 130–170°C. Currently, it is estimated[1] that the manufacture of gypsum plasterboard contributes approximately 3.5% of the UK's annual carbon dioxide emissions. Natural clay plaster[2] has the ecological advantage that no firing is required.

Significant quantities of gypsum plasterboard are recycled from demolition sites, recycling centres and offcuts from building projects. The process requires the removal of paper, insulation materials, timber, fixings and other materials in a specialist gypsum mill. The remaining gypsum can then be recycled into new plasterboards.

Natural Clay Plaster

Clay plasters[2] are manufactured from a blend of unfired natural clays, mixed with minerals and natural pigments. Unlike lime plasters, the material is dried rather than fired at 1000°C, so it is a low embodied energy product. One manufacturer uses the abundant raw materials available in Cornwall. Clay plasters for use in internal walls and ceilings give a breathable finish. The natural pigments give colour which eliminates the need to paint. As they are made entirely from natural products, clay plasters are fully recyclable, compostable and reusable and contain no toxic ingredients or VOCs.

Clay plasters are applied exactly by the same techniques as traditional gypsum plaster to a range of smooth and custom finishes including carving and relief work.

DOI: 10.1201/9781003360469-17

The dry powder is mixed with water for application and any repairs can be replastered as necessary. For smooth finishes, a thickness of 2 mm is typical, rising to 10 mm for heavily textured rustic finishes. A wide range of standard colours is available including RAL® and Pantone® hues. The material helps to regulate internal humidity and is fire resistant to Class 1 (surface spread of flame) to BS 476-7: 1997[3] and Euroclass A1 to BS EN 13501-1: 2018[4] and BS EN 15824: 2017.[5]

Clay plasters can be applied to most internal surfaces including plasterboard and gypsum, but not to wood, MDF or OSB. Very rough surfaces require a straightening coat of lime or clay. The material should not be applied to wet surfaces, but it can be used in areas of high humidity such as kitchens and bathrooms. However, clay plasters are not suitable for wet rooms, showers or in locations where fire sprinklers may be tested. A waterproof finish is available if required. Clay plasters have low embodied carbon in the range of 0.048–0.068 $kgCO_{2e}$/kg. The thermal conductivity for smooth finishes is $\lambda = 0.84$ W/mK, and for rustic finishes $\lambda = 0.97$ W/mK.

Clay Lime Plaster

Clay lime plaster[6] is manufactured from natural materials such as unfired clay, marble, and limestone with added hydraulic lime. The material is VOC free, biodegradable and recyclable. A selection of colours is available and finishes range from smooth to textured including banding, layering and pearlescent. The material

incorporating crushed marble creates a more dramatic heavily textured finish.

Lime Plaster

Lime plaster is manufactured from a mixture of hydrated lime, hydraulic lime and silica (Quartz) with added biomaterial (crop waste). It can be applied using standard plastering tools and is quick setting. A range of textures from smooth to deeply textured can be formed. Lime plaster is breathable and hygrothermal due to the addition of biomaterial which assists in the regulation of moisture content within the local environment. Lime plaster is not suitable for use on damp backgrounds which must be dried out before application. The thermal conductivity of this blended lime plaster $\lambda = 0.27$ W/mK.

Lime-Based Plasterboard

A novel low-carbon plasterboard, Breathaboard®, manufactured from agricultural waste and lime-based binding agent is an alternative to traditional gypsum-based products.[7] During the production of this material carbon dioxide, previously trapped and collected from other industrial sources such as cement manufacture, is passed over the mixture of agricultural waste and the lime-based binder, which then absorbs CO_2 creating calcium carbonate to give the necessary strength to the product. The hygrothermal product is fire-retardant and is fully compostable at end-of-life.

Insulating Aerogel Plaster

Lime plaster incorporating aerogel beads[8] has a thermal conductivity of $\lambda = 0.026$ W/mK. It is suitable for use internally and externally on masonry walls including where space is restricted or the surface is uneven. The material[8] is non-combustible and is breathable.

References

1. *An alternative to gypsum plasterboard*, Maskell, D., Church, M., Thomson, A., Walker, P. and Robinson, T., 2017, University of Bath. Paper presented at the 8th international conference on structural engineering and construction management, Kandy, Sri Lanka.
2. *Natural clay plasters* (https://clay-works.com), Clayworks, Helston, Cornwall.
3. British Standard BS 476-7: 1997. *Fire tests on building materials and structures. Method of test to determine the classification of the surface spread of flame of products*. BSI, London.
4. British Standard BS EN 13501-1: 2018. *Fire classification of construction products and building elements. Classification using data from reaction to fire tests*. BSI London.
5. British Standard BS EN 15824: 2017. *Specification for external renders and internal plasters based on organic binders.* BSI London.
6. *Clay lime plaster* (https://armourcoat.com/en/products/clay-lime-plaster/), Armourcoat Ltd., Sevenoaks.
7. *Breathable plasterboard* (https://adaptavate.com/breathaboard-breathable-plasterboard/), Adaptavate Ltd., Bristol.
8. *Super-insulating aerogel plaster – Fixit 222* (https://www.backtoearth.co.uk/contact/), 29 June 2023, Back to Earth, Exeter.

CHAPTER 18

Insulation Materials

CONTENTS

Introduction

The majority of traditional inorganic and organic building insulating materials are well documented in standard texts on building materials. Many of the organic insulation materials are based on petrochemical products, and the standard inorganic materials such as glass wool, mineral wool and foamed glass require heat energy in their production.

Table 18.1 gives the thermal conductivities of a range of standard insulation materials and Table 18.2 gives the embodied carbon for a range of insulating materials. The Building Research Establishment publication[1] gives a broad overview of the benefits and limitations of natural fibre insulation materials.

Following the Grenfell disaster, the ban on the use of combustible materials in

DOI: 10.1201/9781003360469-18

Table 18.1 Typical thermal conductivity values of insulating materials

Material	Thermal conductivity (W/mK)	Insulation forms
NATURAL MATERIALS		
Wood fibre	0.038–0.050	semi-rigid boards / batts
Cellulose	0.035–0.040	loose / semi-rigid batts
Hemp	0.038–0.040	semi-rigid slabs / batts
Wool	0.038–0.040	semi-rigid boards / rolls
Flax	0.038–0.040	semi-rigid boards / rolls
Cork	0.038–0.070	boards / granulated
Straw	0.080	loadbearing construction
SYNTHETIC MATERIALS		
Mineral fibre	0.032–0.044	boards / semi-rigid boards / rolls
Glass fibre	0.038–0.041	boards / semi-rigid boards / rolls
Extruded polystyrene	0.033–0.035	boards
Expanded polystyrene	0.037–0.038	boards
Polyurethane (PUR)	0.023–0.026	boards
Polyisocyanurate (PIR)	0.023–0.026	boards
Hempcrete	0.060	cast material
Cellular glass	0.041	cast material
Phenolic foam	0.020	boards
Aerogel	0.014	cast material

Notes: BRE Information Paper IP 18/11 Low-Impact Building Materials, Natural Fibre Insulation.
Greenspec, 'Insulation materials and their properties', (https://www.greenspec.co.uk/building-design/insulation-materials-thermal -properties/).

external walls, which came into force in 2018, applies to all residential buildings over 11 m (Scotland has different regulations). Elements attached to the façade, such as upstands for parapet walls, balconies and terraces, all fall within the scope of the ban. The ban applies to bonded materials such as insulation attached to a facing board. The combined unit must be professionally tested to comply with the regulation and only products classified as Euroclass A1 or A2-s1,d0[2] are compliant with the code.

Mineral Wool

A recent advancement has been the improved thermal conductivity of the mineral

Table 18.2 Embodied carbon in insulating materials

Insulating material	Carbon kgCO$_{2e}$/kg
Cork	0.19
Glass wool	1.35
Expanded polystyrene	3.29
Flax	1.70
Paper wool	0.63
Polyurethane rigid foam	4.26
Rockwool	1.12
Wood fibre board	0.98

Note: Data from Inventory of Carbon and Energy v. 2.0, 2011 – Hammond, G. and Jones, C., University of Bath.

wool product NyRock® (λ = 0.032 W/mK) that is manufactured from natural volcanic rock.[3] The improved material has longer fibre lengths which leads to increased encapsulation of air space. Recycled glass cullet, which is unsuitable for sheet glass production, is predominantly used in the production of glass wool insulation. Standard units are 455 × 1200 mm with thicknesses ranging from 50 to 200 mm.

Sheep's Wool

Sheep's wool[4] is a highly efficient sustainable low embodied-energy insulation material with a thermal conductivity that compares favourably to other fibrous insulants. Sheep's wool insulation is available in roll or slab form and either as 100% sheep's wool or blended with 25% polyester fibres. Sheep's wool is generally available in a range of thicknesses from 50 to 200 mm. As wool is potentially susceptible to mould, insects and rodents, some products are treated with chemical agents, such as borax; others are plasma treated to make the fibres unpalatable to potential vermin. Treatment follows washing to remove the natural lanolin oil from the fibres.

The roll material is ideal for loft insulation, while the slabs are convenient for wall and roof insulation. As sheep's wool is a hygroscopic material, it reversibly absorbs and releases water vapour. In summer the material releases moisture and in winter temperatures it absorbs moisture up to 30% of its weight without loss of insulating properties.

Sheep's wool is predominantly non-flammable as it chars when exposed to flame. As a natural material, it is highly eco-friendly and can be recycled or composted at end-of-life, although sheep do produce some methane. In addition to its thermal properties, sheep's wool acts as an effective acoustic insulator.

Sheep's wool insulation (Figure 18.1) is suitable for insulating roofs, walls, lofts and floors. The loose material will fill joints, cracks and hollow spaces. 100% sheep's wool in roll or slab form has a thermal conductivity of λ = 0.036 W/mK. The equivalent 75% wool/25% polyester blend has a thermal conductivity of λ = 0.039 W/mK. The thermal conductivity of loose wool insulation is in the range λ = 0.038–0.040 W/mK.

Hemp Fibre

One form of natural fibre insulation (Figure 18.2) is manufactured from a mixture

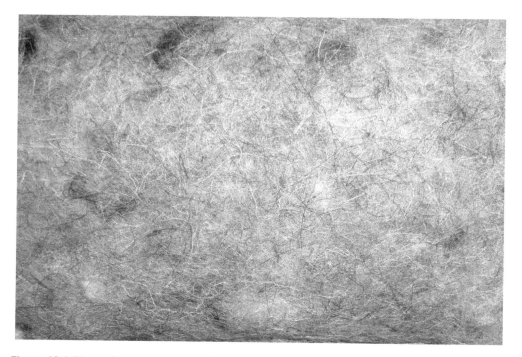

Figure 18.1 Thermafleece® sheep's wool insulation. Photograph: Arthur Lyons

Figure 18.2 Hemp fibre mat insulation. Photograph: Courtesy of Mirreco®

of hemp and flax. Hemp is a fast-growing crop (Figure 18.3) and is produced in several parts of the UK, giving reduced the transportation costs. In Australia, it can produce 3 crops per annum and sequester 22 tonnes of CO_2 per hectare in the 3–4 months growing cycle. IndiTherm® (Figure 18.4) is available as batts or semi-rigid acoustic and

Figure 18.3 Field of fast-growing hemp in West Australia. Photograph: Courtesy of Mirreco®

thermal insulation boards.[5] As a natural material, it offers overall large carbon savings associated with its carbon capture (–0.70kg CO_2eq/kg). The hemp-based products have the advantage of stabilising internal temperatures and humidity. The material is soft to handle, easy to cut on site and thicknesses range from 50 to 140 mm. The thermal conductivity of batts lies in the range λ = 0.038–0.040 W/mK and for insulating board

λ = 0.041 W/mK. Standard dimensions are 1200 × 370, 440 and 570 mm with thicknesses of 50, 80, 90, 100 and 140 mm.

A slightly different product, Ecological Building Systems®, is a blend of 63% hemp and 22% jute fibres with polymer (PET) binding and soda fire retardant[6] (Figure 18.5). The jute fibre is recycled coffee and cocoa bean sacks. Standard sizes are 375 or 580 × 1200 mm with thicknesses

of 40, 60 or 100 mm. The thermal conductivity is λ = 0.039 W/mK and the Euroclass fire classification is E.

An alternative hemp-based insulation, Thermafleece NatraHemp®, is a blend of 60% hemp, 30% recycled polyester and 10% polyester binder.[7] Standard widths are 375 or 570 × 1200 mm with thicknesses of 50, 70 or 100 mm. The thermal conductivity is λ = 0.04239 W/mK and the flammability classification to BS 5803–4: 1985[8] is pass. The product is ultimately recyclable.

Figure 18.5 Jute insulation – Combi Jute® manufactured by Thermo Hanf, Germany. Photograph: Arthur Lyons

Wood Fibre

Wood fibre insulation boards, available with square or tongue & groove profile, are available in 40, 60 and 80 mm thickness to standard sizes of 1325 and 2230 × 600 mm. The material is manufactured from forest thinning and small-diameter logs from sustainable and FSC® and PEFC® registered sources. Steico® rigid insulation boards (Figure 18.6) have a thermal conductivity ranging from λ = 0.04 W/mK to λ = 0.05 W/mK with densities in the range 70 to 230 kg/m³. Enhanced moisture-resistant products are available for use in various applications including behind façades or tiles.[9]

Figure 18.6 Steico® wood fibre insulation. Photograph: Arthur Lyons

The wet and dry manufacturing processes lead to slightly different products.[10] The wet process boards have higher densities, giving better sound absorption but higher thermal conductivity and are ideal for internal wall insulation. The dry process boards are typically used for roof and timber-frame wall applications.

In the wet manufacturing process, chipped timber is ground up and boiled in water to break down the wood into fibres. The slurry is then compressed to remove the water and reheated in steam to bond the fibres together into boards of 20 mm thickness. These are then laminated using water glass (sodium silicate) bonding agent to the required thickness up to 120 mm.

In the dry process, the wood fibres are mixed with 3–4% polyurethane glue (polymeric methylene diphenyl diisocyanate) followed by compression to the required thickness usually in the range of 20–200 mm. The dry process is less energy intensive than the wet process.

At end-of-life the material can be recycled, subject to dismantling and detachment from other products.

Cellulose

Cellulose fibre insulation (Figure 18.7) is manufactured by the fiberisation of recycled newspaper and other organic waste.[11] It is treated with borax for fire resistance, which also makes it unattractive to vermin, insects, fungus and dry rot. The material is not in the form of batts but is blown into the relevant spaces with a purpose-built machine

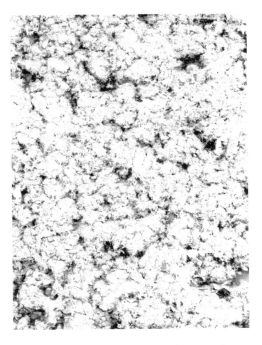

Figure 18.7 Termex® cellulose fibre insulation. Photograph: Arthur Lyons

that breaks up the material into fine particles, which then fill the void spaces, eliminating thermal bridging. The material is therefore applicable to both new build and retrofit. Cellulose insulation also has good sound-absorbing properties. The material smoulders and chars rather than melts when subjected to fire and does not produce any toxic substances (Typical fire designation C-s1,d0). Recycled cellulose has a low embodied energy compared to traditional mineral wool and glass fibre insulation. It can be recycled again or disposed of safely without creating toxic waste. Cellulose fibre insulation has a thermal conductivity in the range $\lambda = 0.035$–0.040 W/mK. A flat ceiling with 400 mm of cellulose insulation has a U-value of $U_c = 0.10$ W/m^{2}K.

An alternative material[12] is produced from a blend of shredded waste paper and hemp or textile fibre. A blend of 70% waste paper and 30% textile fibre has a thermal conductivity of $\lambda = 0.036$ W/mK (Figure 18.8) and a blend of 80% shredded waste paper with 20% hemp has a thermal conductivity of $\lambda = 0.042$ W/mK (Figure 18.9).

Cellulose insulation manufactured as ClearFiber® in the USA is formed in a patented wet process from corrugated cardboard.[13] The cardboard is pulped into a slurry when contaminants such as glue, tape and staples are removed. Liquid borate fire retardant is then added and the slurry is pressed to half its volume. The semi-solid is then broken into pieces prior

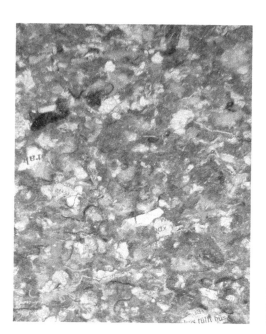

Figure 18.8 Baltic® insulation manufactured from 70% waste paper and 30% textile fibre. Photograph: Arthur Lyons

Figure 18.9 Baltic® insulation manufactured from 80% waste paper and 20% hemp fibre. Photograph: Arthur Lyons

to rotary drying to produce the final fluffy insulation material. It is argued that the supply of newsprint is diminishing, but the availability of corrugated cardboard waste is large and likely to remain buoyant in the foreseeable future.

Mineral Insulating Foam

Airium® is a cement-based aqueous foam which can fill any shape or cavity either on site or in factory-produced units.[14] It is fire-resistant, VOC-free and 100% recyclable. As the material is largely encapsulated air it has a thermal conductivity in the range $\lambda = 0.035$–0.060 W/mK with a compressive strength in the range 20–500KPa. The cement foam is appropriate for use in roofs, walls and floors.

Foamed Glass

Cellular or foamed glass (CG) is a well-established insulation material for roofs and floors, particularly where high loads are anticipated. The newer version of this material is the granular form which is 20% glass and 80% air, making it one of the lightest filling materials available. It is manufactured from 100% recycled glass which is unsuitable for reforming into new glassware. Glapor® has a thermal conductivity of $\lambda = 0.083$ W/mK.[15]

Biopolymer Foams

Standard rigid foams used in construction, such as polyurethane and polystyrene, are petrochemical-based products which have environmental consequences in their production and end-of-life disposal. Approximately 27% of rigid polyurethane foam production is wasted and incinerated, recycled or sent to landfill sites. Incineration is problematic as rigid polyurethane foams generate toxic and carcinogenic fumes when burnt. The new generation of rigid construction foams are based on biopolymers which are less energy intensive in their extraction and will degrade naturally at end-of-life or be used as biofuel. The new biopolymer foams are manufactured from natural materials. Additives may be incorporated to increase moisture resistance, fire retarding properties and to give ultraviolet protection.

Current research is investigating a wide range of plant-based polyols as replacements for the petroleum-based materials used in the current manufacture of polyurethane foam.[16,17] Potential starting materials include kelp, hemp, lignin, soy, rapeseed oil, castor oil, malic acid, tannins and flavonoids. The addition of graphene oxide (GO) to the natural polymers enhances the insulation properties and the flame-retardant performance of the polyurethane foam produced. The new bio-based polyurethane foams have a carbon footprint of 70% less than traditional polyurethane and contain no harmful chemical, noxious stabilisers or toxic additives. The new products can be used for spray foaming or panel insulation.

Icynene® soft foam[18] is an insulation based on castor oil rather than petrochemical products. Castor oil plants (Ricinus communis) are largely grown in India, China and Brazil for their oil.

Icynene soft foam is an open-cell spray-on plastic insulation. The composition is predominantly a mixture of polymeric diphenylmethane diisocyanate and related compounds producing a polyurethane-type material. Icynene is a water-blown foam, so does not contain any CFCs or HCFCs and has no detectable emissions. The fire rating when set behind a 12 mm gypsum board is B-s1,d0 to BS EN 13501–1: 2018 and Class F when exposed.[19] The thermal conductivity is $\lambda = 0.038$ W/mK at a density of 8.3 kg/m^3.

Icynene soft foam is suitable for insulation of walls, roofs and floors but it should not be exposed in habitable rooms where it must be protected behind a 12.5 mm plasterboard for fire protection. The open-cell structure allows the passage of water vapour. In some locations at risk of interstitial condensation, a vapour control barrier may be required.

Mycelium Panels

Mycelium, the fine fibres from fungi, typically mushrooms, which naturally grow underground, can be cultivated and used to create building blocks.[20] Farm crop waste, such as corn-field waste, is finely chopped and blended with mycelium and cast into block moulds. After a few days of growth, the units become solid blocks which can be used for insulation or construction. Once dried out, the material is strong, water, mould and fire-resistant. As the material is organic and non-toxic it can be composted at the end of its useful life in buildings. The material has the advantage that it can easily be grown in any location including on the building site – eliminating transport. Alternative media for mycelium growth are sawdust, sugarcane residues and even building site organic waste. Large blocks can easily be cut or smaller brick units can be cultivated. Once the mycelium has solidified the block it is gently heated to prevent mushroom growth. Mycelium has the advantage that it does not contain any synthetic resin-based compounds which can give off toxic fumes within a fire and it uses waste material that would otherwise go to landfill sites.

Mycelium blocks are light with an average density of 43 kg/m^3 compared to brickwork at 2400 kg/m^3. However, their crushing strength is only 0.2 MPa compared to bricks at 28 MPa, so they can only be used in non-load-bearing structures and for insulation. Biohm® mycelium insulation (Figure 18.10) has a thermal conductivity of $\lambda = 0.03$ W/mK and offers good acoustic absorption. Mycelium rigid insulation boards are available to 1200 × 2400 mm, but the material can be grown to any desired form such as the inner cavity of SIPs (structural insulated panels).

Flax

Flax insulation boards are made from a blend of flax and polyester binder.[21] Flax originated in India, but one current source is a by-product of the linen industry and is therefore only available in relatively small quantities. Flax is treated with boron fire retardant and biocide for durability. Flax insulation in semi-rigid boards or rolls has a thermal conductivity in the range

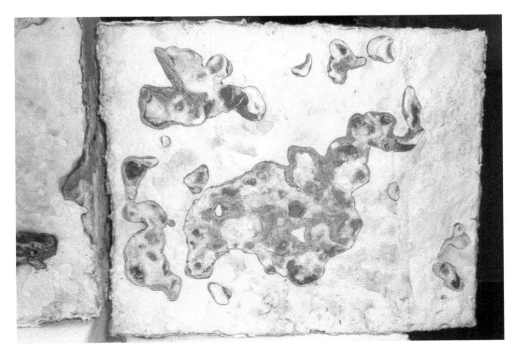

Figure 18.10 Biohm® mycelium insulation. Photograph: Arthur Lyons

λ = 0.38–0.040 W/mK. Typical sizes are 600 × 1000 mm to thicknesses of 50 and 100 mm.

Sisal

Sisal[22] is a strong fibre crop that was traditionally used for making rope and sacks, but is now available as a natural insulation material (Figure 18.11). Sisal is a drought-resistant crop grown in Tanzania which requires little water. The material is blended recycled sheep's wool waste from the Harris Tweed industry together with a starch-based binder and Ecolan® moth-proofing to form carbon-neutral insulation batts. At end-of-life the material is compostable. The vapour-permeable material is appropriate for installation between joists, rafters, within stud walls and in timber-frame construction. The standard batt size is 570 × 1200 mm with a thickness of 100 mm. Sisal/recycled wool insulation has a typical thermal conductivity of λ = 0.036 W/mK and a Euroclass fire rating of E.

Straw

Straw can be used as infill insulation in timber-frame structures.[23] The University of Nottingham Gateway Building is

Figure 18.11 Sisaltech® sisal natural fibre insulation. Photograph: Arthur Lyons

constructed as a cross-laminated timber frame filled with compressed straw insulation (Figures 18.12 and 18.13). Externally the building is finished with a vapour-permeable render but internally the straw infill is exposed as a feature.

Coconut Fibre

Coconut fibre insulation[24] is manufactured from the coconut husk by Enkev®. The majority of the fibre husk is considered to be a waste product as the food industry only

Figure 18.12 University of Nottingham Sutton Bonington Campus building insulated with straw infill. Photograph: Arthur Lyons

uses the edible parts of the coconut. The fibres contain lignin and are therefore tough and durable. To manufacture an insulating board, the fibres are spun into rope, which is then converted to coir sheets and sprayed with renewable natural rubber latex to give elasticity. The latex used is anti-microbial, dust mite resistant and non-allergic. Coconut insulation has an open and resilient structure making the panels potentially appropriate for use as thermal and acoustic insulation in buildings.

Cork

Cork is a well-established insulation material (Figure 18.14), but is included in this text due to its environmental credentials.

Cork is harvested from the cork oak tree, usually on a nine-year cycle (Figures 18.15 and 18.16). The natural material is granulated and then formed under heat and pressure into boards or blocks. The natural resin within the cork acts as a binder. The boards or blocks are then trimmed to standard sizes or to a taper for creating falls for flat roofs. Cork has the advantage over synthetic polymers in that it is unaffected by the application of hot bitumen in flat roofing systems. Insulating cork board (ICB) is described in the standard BS EN 13170: 2012 + A2: 2018.[25]

Cork is also well established for flooring giving a comfortable finish which is mould and mildew resistant, hypoallergenic, antimicrobial and offers noise-reducing

Figure 18.13 Internal detail showing the visually accessible straw insulation in the University of Nottingham, Bonington Campus building. Photograph: Arthur Lyons

qualities. Cork insulation has a thermal conductivity in the range λ = 0.38–0.070 W/mK depending on density.

Eelgrass

Eelgrass (seagrass) (Figure 18.17) which is a natural seaweed, was historically used on the island of Læsø in Denmark for thatching. The material is fire and rot resistant, non-toxic and with insulation properties similar to mineral wool. The material also has the advantage of being easily recycled. It has been used experimentally for small-scale traditional Læsø thatching, but may be potentially used for thermal insulation batts. Panels made with eelgrass also offer an interior acoustic solution to dampen sound levels.

Figure 18.14 Cork insulation. Photograph: Arthur Lyons

Aerogel

Aerogel is a lightweight hydrophobic silica material manufactured by solvent evaporation from silica gel under reduced pressure.[26] It is highly porous and consists of between 95% and 97% airspace with only 3% to 5% of solid material. This limits heat transfer making the material highly insulating with a thermal conductivity of typically λ = 0.014 W/mK.

Aerogel is available as a 10 mm thick blanket bonded to a 3 mm magnesium oxide board with insulation properties equivalent to much thicker standard insulation systems. Typical board size is 1200 × 600 × 13 mm. Aerogel has a fire rating of C-s1,d0. ArmaGel ®HTL is available in rolls of 5, 10 and 20 mm thicknesses with a width of 1.5 m for high-temperature applications such as the

Figure 18.15 Cork trees after harvesting. Photograph: Arthur Lyons

insulation of pipes, vessels and equipment up to 650°C.

Biochar

Biochar[27] is a novel material formed by the pyrolysis of biomass in temperatures ranging from 400 to 800°C in the absence of oxygen. The material has very low thermal conductivity as its micro-pores can trap and immobilise large quantities of air and it is able to absorb moisture up to five times its weight. Clearly the material has variations according to the different biomass feedstocks that are used. Starting materials include bamboo, sugarcane and rice straw but the potential for other materials such as chicken and farmyard manure is extensive.

Figure 18.16 Cork harvest. Photograph: Arthur Lyons

Biochar's low thermal conductivity and ability to absorb large quantities of water make it a useful material for thermal insulation and regulating humidity. In combination with clay, lime or cement mortar, biochar can be used as an additive, up to a maximum of 80% content, for internal plastering or for the formation of bricks and blocks. Additionally, biochar plaster or clay can be applied to external walls using standard plastering spray or hand equipment. A thickness of up to 200 mm biochar can be an alternative to the application of standard expanded polystyrene.

Biochar-clay plasters absorb unwanted smells in domestic kitchens and in large highly frequented spaces they can improve air quality by controlling humidity within the range of 45–70%. In addition, biochar is an efficient absorber of electromagnetic radiation arising from wireless technology and mains electricity. The material mixes are grey in colour but can be painted with clay-based paints as required. At end-of-life, the material can be composted.

Figure 18.17 Eelgrass. Photograph: Arthur Lyons

Vacuum Insulation Panels

One fully encapsulated vacuum insulation panel (VIP) system (Recticel®) offers ultra-high thermal performance for flat roof and terrace applications.[28] The 60 mm thick vacuum panels necessarily are encapsulated in a protective case of PIR foam to ensure no loss of the vacuum during installation. The core material has a thermal conductivity of typically $\lambda = 0.006$ W/mK giving an overall figure of $\lambda = 0.008$ W/mK for the units.

An alternative system (Vacupor®) incorporates a microporous silica core of very low thermal conductivity at low pressure encapsulated by a metalized multi-layer plastic film.[29] One or both sides of the units are covered with sound-absorbent material or a rubber protection layer depending on the application. Typical applications include internal floors and flat roofs. The typical thermal conductivity at 1mbar internal pressure is $\lambda = 0.005$ W/mK and with ambient internal pressure, the thermal conductivity is λ = 0.019 W/mK.

Gas-Filled Panels

Gas-filled insulation panels consist of pockets of low-conductivity gas within a honeycomb of metal foil. The sealed outer layers are manufactured from an aluminium/polymer laminate and the inner honeycomb structure is formed from aluminised low-emissivity films which open up to give the required 38 mm panel thickness. The units can be filled with argon, krypton, xenon or air according to the thermal resistance required. If punctured, the inert gas fill is gradually replaced by air, but the honeycomb structure prevents deflation. One product[30] is supplied flat, to be filled with the appropriate gas on installation. Argon is the standard inert gas fill, but potentially krypton and xenon which give higher thermal resistance values, could be used although these gases are more expensive. Clearly as the inert gases are part of the natural atmosphere, no hazard is produced by leakages.

Hydroceramics

Researchers at the Institute for Advanced Architecture of Catalonia[31] are investigating the use of hydrogels to passively control internal room temperatures by as much as 5°C under hot summer conditions. Hydrogels are polymers which can reversibly absorb up to 400 times their weight of water. Under hot internal temperatures, the contained water evaporates

slowly producing cooling. Current research is investigating the incorporation of hydrogels into 'hydroceramics' – a clay and fabric substrate for incorporation into internal walls. The fabric layer acts as the medium to transport moisture to and from the hydrogel units located within the clay substrate thereby accelerating the absorption and evaporation processes. Then the evaporation of moisture from the clay ceramic produces the cooling effect. The technology has the potential to act as an effective passive cooling system, reducing air-conditioning energy requirements.

Recycled Plastic

Recycled plastic loft insulation[32] material (Figure 18.18) is manufactured from PET (polyethylene terephthalate) from which plastic bottles are made. Bottles are ground up and then extruded into polyester fibre. The rolls of material contain no VOCs and have no loose fibres which could cause skin irritation. The material typically contains 95% recycled material. It is soft to the touch and contains no harmful binders or chemicals. The manufacture of recycled plastic insulation offers a good re-use for the large quantities of single-use plastics which should not be wasted and end up in landfill sites. The material is available in rolls of 50, 100 and 150 mm thicknesses and in widths of 390 and 590 mm to fit between standard timber spacings. In addition to loft and floor insulation, the material is suitable for acoustic insulation in internal walls. The material can be recycled again at end-

Figure 18.18 Recycled plastic insulation manufactured from polyethylene terephthalate (PET) plastic bottles

of-life. The typical thermal conductivity of recycled plastic is λ = 0.040 W/mK and the fire classification is Euro Class E.

Recycled Cotton

Thermo-acoustic insulation, Pavatextil P®, is manufactured from a mixture of 85% cotton and 15% polyester fibres from recycled textiles.[33] The cotton fibres are hydrophilic and hygroscopic which assist in stabilising internal environmental conditions. The fibres are treated with anti-bacterial and fungal agents to give mould and insect resistance also flame retardant. The material is used in conjunction with a vapour barrier within timber or steel framework systems, also for loft insulation. Standard units are 1200 × 600 × 100 mm with thermal conductivity of λ = 0.039 W/mK. The reaction to fire according to BS EN 13501–1:2018[19] is E.

Thermo-Reflective Products

Thermo-reflective insulation systems consist of multi-layers of aluminium foil, fibrous materials and cellular plastics. They act as insulants by reducing conduction, convection and radiation. A wide range of products is available using different combinations plastic foam, plastic bubble sheet, non-woven fibrous wadding and plain or reinforced aluminium foil.

Hybris® consists of a honeycomb of polyethylene foam, layers of reflective aluminium foil and an external copper-coloured layer[34] (Figure 18.19). The metallic layers prevent air infiltration from the outside and the internal honeycomb structure inhibits heat transfer by convection. The low-emissivity external layers enhance the overall thermal resistance. (Emissivity of internal surface e = 0.06 and external face e = 0.10). The material also acts as an acoustic insulant as it is air-sealed. The material is suitable for installation between floor joists, roof rafters and within timber stud walls. Variations include the incorporation of a vapour control layer or a breather membrane. The typical thermal conductivity is $\lambda = 0.033$ W/mK.

Airtight Membrane

The emphasis on airtightness within the latest Building Regulations[35] has given impetus to the enhancement of airtight building membranes. The Wraptite®

Figure 18.19 Actis Hybris® reflective closed cell honeycomb insulation. Photograph: Arthur Lyons

Figure 18.20 Wraptite self-adhesive airtight membrane. Photograph: Courtesy of A. Proctor Group

system[36] (Figure 18.20) is a vapour-permeable, airtight, self-adhering membrane which is applicable externally for most forms of construction. The membrane has a resistance to penetration of air of $0.1m^3/m^2$.hr @ 50 Pa. This type of membrane if installed correctly should create a full wall and roof airtight envelope enabling buildings to comply with the required Building Regulation leakage rates.

All new dwellings must be pressure tested and comply with the current maximum target for air tightness of $<8m^3/m^2h$@50 Pa, which will drop to $<5m^3/m^2h$@50 Pa with the pending Future Homes Standard in 2025.

Modular buildings are frequently delivered on site wrapped in an airtight membrane to ensure that no physical or weather damage occurs during the construction period. Wraptite®, a three-layer tough laminate, has a fire rating of Class B, s1 d0 to BS EN 13501–1:2018.[19] It is available in rolls of 50 m × 1.5 m.

An alternative product by Novia®, manufactured from polypropylene and metallised polypropylene is an air leakage barrier and vapour control layer (VCL) which enhances U-values by virtue of its surface high reflectivity and low emissivity.[37] It is appropriate for use in walls, roofs and floors where high-moisture resistance is required in accordance with BS 5250: 2021.[38] As with all airtight membranes, it requires careful sealing at the joints with specialist tape. It is available in 50 m rolls of 1.5 m width. Reaction to fire is Class E to BS EN 13501–1: 2018.[19]

References

1. BRE Information Paper IP 18/11, *Natural fibre insulation. An introduction to low-impact building materials*, Sutton, A., Black, D. and Walker, P., 2011, IHS Press, Watford.

2. European Reaction to Fire classification (EuroClass) A1 – non-combustible, A2 – limited combustibility.

3. *Nyrock – The lowest lambda stone wool insulation in the UK*, (https://www.rockwool.com/uk/productand-applications/product-overview/nyrock-solutions/), Rockwool UK, Bridgend.

4. *Thermafleece – The UK's only British sheep's wool insulation*, (https://thermafleece.com), Natural Insulations, Soulands Studios Ltd., Penrith.

5. *Inditherm – A flexible thermal insulation batt made from UK crops*, (https://www.indinature.co/inditherm), Industrial Nature UK Ltd., Jedburgh.

6. *Hemp flax thermo hemp combi jute*, (https://www.ecologicalbuildingsystems.com/product/thermo-hemp-combi-jute), Ecological Building Systems UK Ltd., Carlisle.

7. *Thermafleece natrahemp*, (https://thermafleece.com/product/thermafleece-natrahemp), Thermafleece, Penrith.

8. British Standard BS 5803-4: 1985. *Thermal insulation for use in pitched roof spaces in dwellings. Methods for determining flammability and resistance to smouldering*, BSI, London.

9. *Wood fibre: Nature's high-tech insulation material*, (https://www.steico.com/en/solutions/product-advantages/steico-insulation-materials/), Steico, Feldkirchen.

10. *Wood fibre insulation – Manufacturing processes*, (https://www.greenspec.co.uk/wood-fibre-manufact-process/), Greenspec, Beverley.

11. *Termex cellulose insulation*, (https://termex.fi/en/home), Termex, Saarijärvi, Finland.

12. *Thermal insulation from waste paper and hemp*, (https://www.balticfloc.lv/en/publications/), Balticfloc, Cesis, Latvia.

13. *CleanFiber high performance building insulation from recycled corrugated cardboard*, (https://www.43north.org/), 43North, Buffalo, New York.

14. *Airium – A revolution in insulation*, (https://www.holcim.com/media/meda-releases/airium-revolution-in-insulation), Holcim, Zug, Switzerland.

15. *Glapor recycled foamed glass*, (https://www.lime.org.uk/), Tŷ-Mawr, Brecon, Powys.

16. *Alternatives derived from renewable natural fibre to replace conventional polyurethane rigid foam insulation*,

Murmu, S.B., Cleaner Engineering and Technology, Vol. 8, Article 100513, June 2022, Elsevier, Amsterdam.

17. *Bio-based rigid polyurethane foam from castor oil with excellent flame retardancy and high insulation capacity via cooperation with carbon-based materials.* Acuna, P., Zhang, J. et al. Journal of Materials Science, Vol. 56, pp. 2684–2701, 2021, Springer, Berlin.

18. *Castor oil based foam for wall insulation – is it viable?*, (https://www.homelogic.co.uk/castor-oil-based-foam-for-wall-insulation-is-it-viable), Home Logic UK Ltd., Southampton.

19. British Standard BS EN 13501-1: 2018. *Fire classification of construction products and building elements. Classification using data from reaction to fire tests*, BSI, London.

20. *Mycelium*, (https://www.biohm.co.uk/mycelium), Biohm, London.

21. *Flax-based insulation. Natural thermal and acoustic insulation for timber frame, partitions, lofts, roofs and floors*, 2022, Greenspec, Beverley.

22. *Sisaltech sustainable insulation*, (https://sisaltech.com), Sisaltech, Roslin, Midlothian.

23. *Straw bale: An introduction to low impact building materials*, BRE IP 15/11Sutton, A., Black, D. and Walker, P., BRE, Watford.

24. *Thermal-acoustic insulation-Cocolok*, (https://enkev.com/natural-products/cocolok), Volendam, Holland.

25. BS EN 13170: 2012 + A2: 2018. *Thermal insulation products for buildings. Factory made products of expanded cork (ICB). Specification*, BSI, London.

26. *Innovative aerogel insulation blanket technology*, (https://local.armacell.com/en/armagel/insulation-products/), Armacell, Luxembourg.

27. *The use of biochar as building material*, Schmidt, H.P., The Biochar Journal 2014, ISSN 2297-1114, (www.biochar-journal.org/en/ct/3), Version of 12 May 2014, Arbaz, Switzerland.

28. *What is a vacuum insulation panel?*, (https://www.recticelinsulation.com/), Recticel Insulation, Stoke-on-Trent.

29. *Vacupor MS – vacuum insulation panel*, (https://morganthermalceramics.com/media/4556/vacupor-ms-data-sheet-english.pdf), Morgan Advanced Materials, Stourport-on-Severn.

30. *Innovative gas-filled panel insulation from Fi-Foil*, (https://www.building-ggreen.com/news-article/innovative-gas-filled-panel-insulation-fi-foil), BuildingGreen, Fi-Foil Company, Florida.

31. *Hydroceramic*, Institute of Advanced Architecture of Catalonia, (https://iaac.net/project/hydroceramic/), Barcelona.

32. *Recycled plastic insulation made from plastic bottles*, (https://supasoftinsulation.com), Eden Renewable Innovations Ltd., Penrith.

33. *Pavatextil P - Cotton fibre-based thermos-acoustic insulation*, (https://www.soprema.co.uk/), Soprema, Witham.

34. *Hybris*, (https://www.insulation-actis.com/hybrid-system/hybris-uk.html), Actis Insulation Ltd., Chippenham.

35. Building Regulations, Conservation of fuel and power: Approved Document Part L – updated 2

February 2023 (applies to England). UK Government.

36. *Wraptite external air tightness barrier*, (https://wwwproctorgroup.com/air-barriers), A Proctor Group, Blairgowrie, Perth.

37. *Novia vapour control layers*, (https://novia.co.uk/vapour-control-layers), Novia, Sittingbourne, Kent.

38. British Standard BS 5250: 2021. *Management of moisture in buildings. Code of practice*, BSI, London.

CHAPTER 19

Paints and Surface Treatments

CONTENTS

Introduction

The paint industry continues its emphasis on switching to water-based paints in order to reduce the harmful effects on the atmosphere of emitting noxious volatiles (VOCs). The more eco-friendly clay and lime-based paints are becoming more popular as non-traditional construction materials such as hemp, lime, straw and compacted earth become familiar within the building industry.

Natural Paints

Many paints contain VOCs (Volatile Organic Compounds) some of which can be harmful to health and the environment. Other VOCs are necessarily present in the material and like natural perfumes are not harmful to the atmosphere. The quantity of harmful volatiles in paints has been regulated since 2010. Natural paints do not contain noxious VOCs such as synthetic chemicals or solvents and are genuinely water-based.

All paints require solvents, fillers, binders and colourants. Natural paints incorporate earth and mineral pigments such as manganese oxide and spinel (magnesium/aluminium oxide) rather than azo dyes as colourants. Additionally, natural paints

DOI: 10.1201/9781003360469-19

incorporate silicates rather than acrylic-based binders which come from the petro-chemical industry. Chalk and clay are the standard extenders and titanium dioxide gives the opacity. Natural oils are used as drying agents and the solvent is water rather than organic VOCs. Additional minor components are plant-based products.

Natural paints are available as emulsion for lime plaster, also eggshell for wood-work and metal. The gloss paint for woodwork and metal is not a high gloss, being water rather than solvent-based; it is however officially classified according to the EU Directive[1] as VOC-free. The range of colours is more restricted than conventional paints due to the use of only naturally occurring pigments rather than azo dyes.

Ultra-White Paint

Ultra-white paint can reflect 98% of inci-dent visible and infrared sunlight com-pared to standard white paints which reflect typically 80–90% of incident sun-light. The increase in reflectivity means that painted surfaces exposed to sunlight will remain significantly cooler than sur-faces painted white with routine materials. This enhanced protection against heating can in certain circumstances lead to a reduced requirement for building cooling systems. Daytime surface temperatures in strong sunlight can be 4°C cooler than would be anticipated. Ultra-white paint contains a high concentration of barium sulphate particles which are very white and highly reflective. In addition to their reflectivity, sunlight scattering is effected by using a wide range of particle sizes, which gives the maximum scattering of the light spectrum from the sun.

Clay-Based Paint

Clay-based paints are virtually VOC-free and give an odour-free, breathable ultra-matt finish.[2] Compositions vary, but may include clay, sand, chalk, talc (magnesium silicate), methyl cellulose, phosphate and titanium dioxide. One formulation uses a biogenic binding agent which gives a more durable, scratch and dent-resistant finish. Clay paints for internal applications are available in a wide range of mainly pastel shades but also some strong colours.

Lime-Based Paint

Graphenstone® paint is based on lime which is fired in wood-burning ovens that produce a pure white product.[3] Graphene polymer fibres are incorporated in the mix to give flexibility and toughness which enhances durability. The paint products contain no petrochemical-based materials, only a trace of VOCs at less than 0.1% (1 g per litre) and the CO_2 produced in the calcining of the lime is reabsorbed as the lime returns calcium carbonate. The majority of the CO_2 is absorbed within 60 days of application, at the approximate rate of 0.3 kg of CO_2 per litre of paint applied, mitigating that emitted in the manufacturing process. The photo-catalytic option has an antibacterial function to inhibit bacteria and moulds. A range of colours is standard.

Conductive Shielding Paint

One form of conductive shielding paint consists of an aqueous acrylic emulsion incorporating graphene fibres.[4] The graphene content makes the material electrically conductive and gives protection against high- and low-frequency electromagnetic radiation from telephone towers, television transmitters, radio antennas and external WiFi networks. As the material is electrically conductive it is recommended that each painted surface is electrically grounded by a qualified technician. The product, which has low VOC content, has applications in hospitals, schools, warehouses, offices and server rooms. It can be applied to any dry surface including masonry, plaster, mortar and well-adhered old paint.

Self-Cleaning Paint

One self-cleaning paint system incorporates nanoparticles of titanium dioxide which in the presence of sunlight or UV light break down any organic material on the surface of the paint.[5] The surface is also hydrophilic, so water washes over the whole surface area uniformly removing dirt and the degraded mould, fungi and mildew.

An alternative self-cleaning paint[6] system also uses nano-titanium dioxide, but in the presence of a water-repellent surface, which causes the rain to remain as droplets that roll over the surface collecting the dirt before they disperse. The paint incorporates adhesives which are resilient to wiping of the surface so that the self-cleaning effect is retained.

Antimicrobial Coating

One form of antimicrobial coating is based on silver ion technology.[7] In the presence of moisture, silver ions prevent bacteria from converting nutrients into energy, inhibit their cell division and block replication of their DNA. One system uses silver phosphate as the active agent.

The alternative agent used within antimicrobial coatings is titanium dioxide[8] which under low levels of UV light releases reactive oxygen species. These then attack the virus's genetic material, both the proteins that invade the human body and also the fatty sphere that holds the virus together. The virus is quickly killed leaving the surface biologically clean.

An antibacterial coating developed by University College, London, consists of clusters of chemically modified gold embedded in a polymer incorporating crystal violet which has antibacterial and antifungal properties. It is activated by low-intensity ambient light and kills *E. Coli* and *Staphylococcus aureus*.[9]

Antipollution Surface Treatment

Surface treatment for concrete and wood containing titanium dioxide nanoparticles can enhance air quality by breaking down toxic gases in polluted areas. The titanium dioxide nanoparticles act as photocatalysts in the presence of UV/daylight to convert NO_x gasses into harmless nitrates. In addition to removing noxious nitrogen and sulphur oxides, the antimicrobial property of Airlite® antipollution surface treatment removes bacteria, moss and algae.

An alternative surface coating (Puri-Face®) (Figure 19.1) which breaks down pollutants such as carbon monoxide (CO) and volatile organic compounds (VOCs) in order to improve internal air quality is under research investigation at University College London (UCL).[10]

Sprayed Cork

Sprayed cork coatings (Figure 19.2) can be applied internally or externally. Externally the material has an expected lifespan of over 20 years and gives an enhanced thermal performance. A wide range of colours is available from pastel shades and grey to

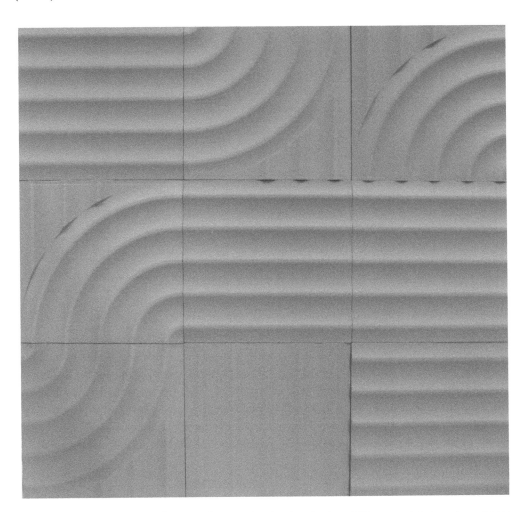

Figure 19.1 Puri-Face® antipollution surface coating that breaks down NO$_x$ gasses into harmless nitrates. Photograph: Arthur Lyons

Figure 19.2 Sprayed cork thermal and acoustic finish. Photograph: Arthur Lyons

strong colours such as ochre, heather and olive. Internally a 6–8 mm coat produces a breathable finish with enhanced thermal and acoustic performance. Sprayed cork has a Euro-class B fire resistance rating. Internally the material can be plastered over for a smooth finish or painted as required.

Water-Splitting Paint

Scientists at the Royal Melbourne Institute of Technology (RMIT) have researched a novel paint containing molybdenum sulphide which absorbs moisture from the air.[11]

In the presence of titanium dioxide, the water is split into hydrogen and oxygen. The hydrogen can then potentially be harvested as a fuel. The process named electrolyteless photocatalytic gas phase water splitting is only in the early experimental stage and requires considerable further development.

References

1. Directive 2004/42/CE of the European Parliament and of the Council on the limitation of emissions of volatile organic solvents in certain paints and

varnishes and vehicle finishing products and amending Directive 1999/13/EC, 21 April 2004.

2. *High grade clay paint*, (https://celticsustainables.co.uk/auro-331-natural-clay-paint), Celtic Sustainables, Cardigan, West Wales.

3. *Eco-friendly paint*, (https://graphenstone-ecopaints.store), Graphenstone, Harleston, Norfolk.

4. *Proshield Premium – Conductive shielding paint with graphene*, (https://grahenstone.co.uk/graphenstone-uk-proshield.html), Graphenstone, Harleston, Norfolk.

5. *Titanium dioxide based self-cleaning smart surfaces. A short review*, Padmanabhan, N.T. and Honey, J., Journal of Environmental Chemical Engineering, Vol. 8, Issue 5, October 2020, Science Direct, Elsevier, Amsterdam.

6. *Researchers develop self-cleaning paint using coated titanium dioxide nanoparticles*, (https://www.pcimag.com), Paints and Coatings Industry, Troy, Michigan, USA.

7. *Electrochemically synthesised silver phosphate coating on anodised aluminium with superior antibacterial properties*, Agbe, H., Sarkar, D.K. and Chen, G., Surface and Coating Technology, Vol. 428, 127892, 25 December 2021, Elsevier Science Direct, Amsterdam.

8. *Antimicrobial TiO_2 nanocomposite coatings for surfaces, dental and orthopaedic implants*, Kumaravel, J.E., Nair, K.M., Mathew, S., Bartlett, J., Kennedy, J.E. et al., Chemical Engineering Journal, Vol. 416, 129072, 2021, Elsevier Science Direct, Amsterdam.

9. *Photobactericidal activity activated by thiolated gold nanoclusters at low flux levels of white light*, Hwang, G.B., Huang, H., Wu, G., Shin, J. et al., 5 March 2020, Nature Communications, London.

10. *Puri-Face* - Surface coating research in collaboration with Dr Gi-Byoung Hwang, (www.mzero.kr and taiho.shin@mzero.kr), University College, London.

11. *Surface water dependent properties of sulphur-rich molybdenum sulphides: Electrolyteless gas phase water splitting* Daeneke, T., Dahr, N., Atkin, P. et al: ACS Nano (American Chemical Society), Vol. 11, pp. 6782–6794, School of Engineering and School of Science, RMIT University, Melbourne.

CHAPTER 20

Biophilic Design

CONTENTS

Introduction

The chapter defines biophilic design and describes its positive effects on human health and well-being particularly in the workplace.

Biophilic Design

Biophilic design[1,2] incorporates live planting within the internal built environment. External planting, such as green roofs and walls (Figure 20.1), is a well-developed part of architectural design, but the inclusion of live planting has only recently come to play a significant part in interior design. Interior planting has a real positive effect on the health and well-being of the occupants and it is considered to enhance performance and productivity in educational environments, health care facilities, offices and commercial workplaces.[3] The concept is to link more closely the bond between ourselves and the natural world at a time when we spend more and more time looking at smartphones and computer screens.

In addition to the incorporation of planting, biophilic design encompasses links to the wider environment through natural lighting and visual contact with exterior spaces, whether it is the sky, trees, a courtyard or a wide open space. It is generally accepted that the presence of living plants within enclosed areas improves the air quality and helps to support physical and mental health.

House plants, such as bamboo, are easy to maintain and provide a good level of humidity. Smaller potted plants and hanging baskets offer good focal points. The presence of planting can reduce stress and accelerate recovery from illness. In addition, biophilic design is enhanced by multi-sensory stimuli such as

DOI: 10.1201/9781003360469-20

Figure 20.1 Green wall on the University of Leicester, George Davies Centre for Medicine. Photograph: Arthur Lyons

water features which encourage tranquillity and gentle airflow which can improve student performance within the classroom.

The variety of fixed internal installations ranges from green walls, room dividers and living wall pictures to traditional potted plants[4-6] (Figures 20.2–20.5). Externally where there is visual contact from internal spaces, green walls and screens can enhance the well-being of occupants. For external screening, Hedera (ivy) has the advantage

Figure 20.2 Internal green wall in the University of Nottingham Research Acceleration and Demonstration building. Photograph: Arthur Lyons

Figure 20.3 Biotecture® green wall system. Photograph: Arthur Lyons

Figure 20.4 Mobilane® internal green screen system showing the planting containers. Photograph: Arthur Lyons

Figure 20.5 Meristem Design® living wall picture with a variety of foliage plants. Photograph: Arthur Lyons

of being evergreen and is available in a range of colour varieties. Pyracantha produces white flowers in the spring followed by a mass of bright red berries in the autumn.

References

1. *Ten beautifully biophilic buildings from Dezeen's Pinterest*, Bah, S., 15 May 2023, Dezeen, London.

2. *Nature inside- a biophilic design guide*, Browning, W.D. and Ryan, C.O., 1 September 2020, RIBA Publishing, London.

3. *Quantitative improvement in workplace performance through biophilic design: A pilot experiment case study*, Sanchez, J.A., Ikaga, T. and Sanchez, S.V., Energy and Buildings, Vol. 177, 2018 pp. 316–328, Elsevier, Amsterdam.

4. *Living hoardings*, (https://www/ biotecture.uk.com), Biotecture Ltd. (Nursery), Chichester.

5. *Building green*, (https://mobilane.com/ en/), Mobilane, London.

6. *Living walls*, (https://www.meristemde sign.co.uk), Meristem Design, London.

CHAPTER 21

Acoustic Control

Introduction

The Building Regulations set the criteria for noise control within and between buildings. This chapter describes the sound insulation requirements for separating walls within new dwellings. The parts of Building Regulations relevant to sound transmission for the four UK Nations are listed.[1–4]

Acoustic Control

Noise pollution is a matter of concern in the home, the workplace and in public open spaces. Building Regulations lay down criteria for the passage of sound within buildings and between adjacent properties. In principle, newly built dwelling houses and flats require 45 dB airborne sound insulation for separating walls, floors and stairs and 62 dB impact sound insulation between separating walls and stairs. Purpose-built rooms for residential purposes require 43 dB impact sound insulation for walls, 45 dB for stairs and 62 dB impact sound insulation for floors and stairs. Slightly reduced requirements are specified for spaces created by a material change of use.

The Building Regulations give extensive examples of how these criteria can be met. Guidance for England is within Approved Document E – 2015,[1] for Wales Guidance Part E – 2003 updated 2010,[2] for Scotland – Building Standards Technical Handbook – Part 5 – 2023[3] and for Northern Ireland Technical Booklet G – 2012.[4] Robust Details® also gives a range of solutions to meet the criteria required by the Building Regulations.[5]

A selection of sound-absorbing materials[6] is illustrated in Figure 21.1.

DOI: 10.1201/9781003360469-21

Figure 21.1 A selection of sound-absorbing panels produced by Acoustic Materials Ltd.®, Ireland. Photograph: Arthur Lyons

Noise pollution in open spaces, particularly near sound sources such as roads and railways can be ameliorated by the use of acoustic screens. Solid sound screens block the direct sound, but general ambient noise can be reduced by the use of timber or steel composite barriers which incorporate sound-absorbing mineral wool. Sound absorption is typically in the range 9–11 dB(A).

References

1. Building Regulations 2010 – Part E – Resistance to the Passage of Sound – Approved Document – for use in England – 2003 edition incorporating 2010, 2013 and 2015 amendments.

2. Building Regulations 2010 - Part E – Resistance to the Passage of Sound – Approved Document – for use in Wales – 2003 edition incorporating 2004 and 2010 amendments.

3. Building Standards Technical Handbook 2023 (Building Scotland Regulations 2004): Domestic buildings – Section 5.

4. Building Regulations Northern Ireland 2012: Part G – Sound insulation of dwellings.

5. *Robust details*, (https://robustdetails.com), Robust Details Ltd., Milton Keynes.

6. *Acoustic materials*, (https://www.acousticmaterials.ie), Acoustic Materials Ltd., Wicklow.

CHAPTER 22

General Recycling

CONTENTS

Introduction

The majority of individual materials manufacturers are recycling surplus materials including offcuts produced within their manufacturing plants for both economic and ecological reasons. Some material suppliers are accepting back offcuts from building sites, but the system is not well organised, and large quantities of building material waste still end up in landfill sites.

Surplus Materials

The Norwegian company Sirken® has instigated a system of selling surplus materials directly from the construction industry.[1] The company sets up an inventory of available materials on all the building sites within their scheme and makes the listing available to participating members. The system avoids large quantities of building materials being sent to waste management sites where a significant quantity would inevitably destroyed as waste. Normally the cost of storing surplus materials is greater than the cost of throwing them away and purchasing new when required. However, this system offers an alternative to the environmentally unfriendly waste of construction materials. It also enables surplus materials to be purchased at reasonable cost, normally within the locality. Typically about 10–15% of the total waste from construction projects can be resold as surplus goods.

Deconstruction and Reuse

The company Rotor DC® is a cooperative[2] in Brussels which organises the reuse of

DOI: 10.1201/9781003360469-22

construction materials. The company deconstructs buildings which otherwise would have been demolished, enabling useful materials to be salvaged, marketed and reused.

Repurposing of Materials

A proposed system to enhance the repurposing of materials from deconstruction sites is to label the materials with a QR code[3] during demolition prior to transportation to storage. The data system would then hold the information on available materials including their location for speedier access for transportation to a new site for reuse.[4] This should reduce the quantities of construction materials which currently end up in landfill sites. Currently, 62% of UK's waste comes from the construction industry and demolition.[5]

References

1. *Sirken turns surplus building materials into valuable commodity*, (https://businessnorway.com/solutions/), Business Norway, Oslo, Norway.
2. *RotorDC Deconstruction and Consulting*, (https://rotordc.com), Brussels.
3. *Using engraved QR codes to connect building components to materials passports for circular construction* Byers, B., Cheriyamulla, S., Ewason, J., Hall, D. et al., 2022 European Conference on Computing in Construction, 24 July 2022, Rhodes, Greece.
4. *How can Material Passports support material re-use of existing buildings?*, Orms Designers and Architects Ltd., London.
5. *Orms proposes 'live' material passports to reduce construction waste*, Lowe, T., 17 May 2021, Building Design, London.

CHAPTER 23

Carbon Storage

CONTENTS

Introduction

Carbon capture and storage (CCS) is currently seen as a positive method of immediately reducing the quantities of carbon dioxide released into the atmosphere by industry, commerce, transport and homes and is supported by the UK government.[1,2] One imminent development will be carbon dioxide storage deep in the depleted North Sea oil fields off the west coast of Scotland. However, long-term, carbon capture, usage and storage (CCUS) is clearly a better option. In this respect, the potential for the permanent sequestering of carbon by the growing and utilisation of hemp and other natural construction materials offers much greater potential for carbon reduction.

Green Carbon Storage

A range of carbon capture and storage methods are under investigation, particularly in relation to the concrete and steel industries as the larger generators of industrial carbon dioxide waste. Both industries are researching carbon capture and storage (CCS) including underwater storage and the use of algae. These options are described in Chapter 11 Cement, Concrete and Clay (page 97) and Chapter 13 – Ferrous and Non-ferrous Metals page 147.

However, Mirreco® in Australia is developing the technology to simply remove carbon dioxide from the air by planting more hemp[3] (Figure 23.1). According to the European Industrial Hemp Association,[4] one hectare of industrial hemp absorbs approximately 10.5 tonnes of carbon dioxide compared to forests which absorb from 2 to 6 tonnes per hectare per year.

Hemp when harvested can be used to produce a wide range of carbon-neutral or carbon-negative products. Hemp has a range

DOI: 10.1201/9781003360469-23

of uses within the construction industry including Hempcrete which is described in Chapter 11 – Cement, Concrete and Clay page 104 and as an insulating material described in Chapter 18 – Insulation Materials page 189. However, hemp can also be converted into bio-fuel and plastics replacing the demand on natural fossil fuel deposits. When harvested and allowed to slowly smoulder, hemp produces tar, and the residue can be returned to the soil, sequestering the remaining carbon dioxide that was absorbed during growth. The commercial growing of hemp may well be encouraged in the future by the award of carbon credits to farmers who are willing to grow the crop.

References

1. *UK carbon capture, use and storage – How the government supports the development of carbon capture, usage and storage (CCUS) in the UK and internationally,* UK Government – Department for Energy Security and Net Zero, 22 January 2013, updated 1 February 2019.
2. *Carbon capture and storage,* BGS Research, British Geological Survey, Nottingham.
3. *Revolutionary hemp manufacturing,* (https://mirreco.com), Mirreco UK Ltd., London.
4. European Industrial Hemp Association conference, Wilson, C., 5 June 2019, Cologne.

Bibliography

Further Reading

Achal, V. and Chin, C.S., 2021, *Building materials for sustainable and ecological environment.* Springer, Berlin.

Aitchison, M., 2018, *Prefab housing and the future of building. Product to process.* Lund Humphries Publishers Ltd., London.

Bayliss, S. and Bergin, R., 2020, *The modular housing handbook.* RIBA Publishing, London.

Chatterton, P., 2014, *Low impact living – A field guide to ecological, affordable community building (Earthscan tools for community planning).* Routledge, Abingdon-on-Thames.

Craswell, P., 2023, *Reclaimed – New homes from old materials.* Thames & Hudson, Melbourne.

Fardis, M.N., 2011, *Innovative materials and techniques in concrete construction – ACES workshop.* Springer, Berlin.

Fernandez, J., 2005, *Material architecture – Emergent materials for innovative buildings and ecological construction.* Routledge, Abingdon-on-Thames.

Frigione, M. and Barroso de Aguiar, J., 2021, *Innovative materials for construction.* MDPI AG, Basel.

Gallagher, M., 2010, *Modern methods of construction. The way forward for the Irish construction industry.* VDM Verlag, Riga.

Gaze, C., Ross, K., Nolan, E. and Novakovic, O., 2007, *Modern methods of construction.* IHS BRE Press, Bracknell.

Hairstans, R., 2010, *Off-site and modern methods of timber construction a sustainable approach.* TRADA Technology Ltd., High Wycombe.

Harris, C. and Borer, P., 2005, *The whole house book – Ecological building design and materials*, 2nd ed. Centre for Alternative Technology Publications, Machynlleth.

Khatib, J., 2016, *Sustainability of construction materials*, 2nd ed. Woodhead Publishing, Sawston.

Lancashire, R. and Taylor, L., 2012, *Innovative timber construction – New ways to achieve energy efficiency.* TRADA Technology Ltd., High Wycombe.

Lewis, P., Tsurumaki, M. and Lewis, D.J., 2022, *Manual of biogenic house sections – Materials and carbon.* ORO Editions, Novato, California.

Lyons, A., 2020, *Materials for architects and builders*, 6th ed. Routledge, Abingdon-on-Thames.

Madsen, D.A. and Madsen, D.P., 2017, *Modern residential construction practices.* Routledge, Abingdon-on-Thames.

Malik, J.A. and Marathe, S., 2021, *Ecological and health effects of building materials.* Springer, Berlin.

Mamlouk, M.S. and Janiewski, J.P., 2017, *Materials for civil and construction engineers – SI Edition*, 4th ed. Pearson, London.

NHBC, 2018, *Modern methods of construction. Who's doing what?*, NF82, NHBC Foundation, Milton Keynes.

Nunan, J., 2009, *The complete guide to alternative home building materials and methods including sod, compressed earth, plaster, straw, beer cans, bottles, cordwood and many other low cost material.* Atlantic Publishing Group Inc., Ocala, Florida.

Ottmann, D.A., 2022, *Ecological building materials for deserts and drylands. (Springer briefs in geography).* Springer, Berlin.

Peck, M., 2014, *Modern concrete construction manual – Structural design, materials, properties, sustainability.* Detail, EPP Professional Publishing Group GmBH, München.

Ross, K., 2005, *Modern methods of house construction – A Surveyors guide.* BRE Trust, Watford.

Sayigh, A., 2021, *The importance of wood in sustainable buildings.* Springer, Berlin.

Sayigh, A., 2022, *Towards net zero carbon emissions in the building industry – Innovative renewable energy.* Springer, Berlin.

Stanwix, W. and Sparrow, A., 2014, *The hempcrete book – Designing and building with hemp-lime.* Green Books, Cambridge.

Vatin, N. (Ed.), 2015, *Innovative technologies in development of construction industry.* Trans. Tech Publications Ltd, Baech, Switzerland.

Watts, A., 2018, *Modern construction handbook*, 6th ed. Birkhauser, Basel.

Watts, A., 2019, *Modern construction case studies – Emerging innovation in construction techniques*, 2nd ed. Birkhauser, Basel.

Woolley, T., 2022, *Natural building techniques. A guide to ecological methods and materials.* The Crowood Press Ltd., Marlborough.

Journals

Building Magazine, Monthly, (building.-co.uk), UBM Built Environment, London.

Concrete Quarterly, (quarterly to) Issue 283, Summer 2023, MPA The Concrete Centre, London.

Glass Times, (monthly to) Volume 17, Issue 8, August 2023, Times Publishing Ltd., Manchester.

Light Steel Framing Magazine, Issue 5, Summer 2022, Radar Communications Ltd., Shrewsbury.

New Steel Construction, (monthly to) Volume 31, No. 7, July/August 2023, Barrett Byrd Associates, Tunbridge Wells.

OffSite, Issue 32, May/Jun 2022 to Issue 38, Jul/Aug 2023, Offsite Media Ltd., Shrewsbury.

Structural Timber, Spring 2022, Radar Communications Ltd., Shrewsbury.

Tall Buildings, Issue 3, Summer 2022 &, Issue 4 Spring 2023, Radar Communications Ltd., Shrewsbury.

Volumetric Modular, Issue 2, Jun/Jul 2022 & Issue 3, Dec/Jan 2023, Radar Communications Ltd., Shrewsbury.

Building Regulations

England

Approved Document B, Fire safety, Volume 1: Dwellings, 2019 edition incorporating 2020 and 2022 amendments.

Approved Document B, Fire safety, Volume 2: Buildings other than dwellings, 2019 edition incorporating 2020 and 2022 amendments.

Approved Document F, Ventilation, 2010, updated 2022.

Approved Document L, Conservation of fuel and power, Volume 1: Dwellings, 2021 edition incorporating 2023 amendments.

Approved Document L, Conservation of fuel and power, Volume 2: Buildings other than dwellings, 2021 edition incorporating 2023 amendments.

Approved Document O, Overheating, 2021, updated 2022.

Wales

Approved Document B, Fire safety, Volume 1: Dwellinghouses, 2006 edition incorporating 2016 and 2020 amendments.

Approved Document B, Fire safety, Volume 2: Buildings other than dwellinghouses, 2006 edition incorporating 2010, 2013, 2016 and 2020 amendments.

Approved Document Part F, Ventilation, 2022.

Approved Document L, Conservation of fuel and power, Volume L1A: New dwellings, 2014 edition incorporating 2016 amendments.

Approved Document L, Conservation of fuel and power, Volume L1B: Existing dwellings, 2014 edition incorporating 2016 amendments.

Approved Document L, Conservation of fuel and power, Volume L2A: New buildings other than dwellings, 2014 edition incorporating 2016 amendments.

Approved Document L, Conservation of fuel and power, Volume L2B: Existing buildings other than dwellings, 2014 edition incorporating 2016 amendments.

Building Regulations Guidance: Part O, Overheating, 2022.

Scotland

Building Standards Technical Handbook 2023: Domestic.

Building Standards Technical Handbook 2023: Non-domestic.

Northern Ireland

Building Regulations (Northern Ireland) 2012, Part E, Fire Safety.

Building Regulations (Northern Ireland) 2012, Part F, Conservation of fuel and power.

Building Regulations (Northern Ireland) 2012, Part K, Ventilation.

British Standards

BS 476-4: 1970 Fire tests on building materials and structures. Non-combustibility test for materials.

BS 476-7: 1997 Fire tests on building materials and structures – Method of test to determine the classification of the surface spread of flame of products.

BS 5250: 2021 Management of moisture in buildings. Code of practice.

BS 5803-4: 1985 Thermal insulation for use in pitched roof spaces in dwellings. Methods for determining flammability and resistance to smouldering.

BS 6375 Performance of windows and doors:

Part 1: 2015 + A1: 2016: Classification for weathertightness and guidance on selection and specification.

Part 2: 2009: Classification for operation and strength characteristics and guidance on selection and specification.

Part 3: 2009 + A1: 2013: Classification for additional performance characteristics and guidance on selection and specification.

BS 8500: 2023 Concrete - Complementary Standard to BS EN 206:
Part 1 Method of specifying and guidance for the specifier.
Part 2 Specification for constituent materials and concrete.

BS 8683: 2021 Process for designing and implementing Biodiversity Net Gain. Specification.

BS 8902: 2009 Responsible sourcing sector certification schemes for construction products. Specification.

BS EN 197-5: 2021 Cement. Portland-composite cement CEMII/C-M and Composite cement CEM VI.

BS EN 206: 2013 + A2: 2021 Concrete. Specification, performance, production and conformity.

BS EN 771-1: 2011 + A1: 2015 Specification for masonry units. Clay masonry units.

BS EN 771-3: 2011 + A1: 2015 Specification for masonry units. Aggregate concrete masonry units (Dense and lightweight aggregates).

BS EN 1096-1: 2012 Glass in Building - Coated Glass. Definitions and Classification.

BS EN 1993-1-2: 2005 Eurocode 3. Design of steel structures. General rules.

BS EN 1995-1-1: 2004 + A2: 2014 Eurocode 5: Design of timber structures. General. Common rules and rules for buildings.

BS EN 10025-5: 2019 Hot rolled products of structural steels. Technical delivery conditions for structural steels with improved atmospheric corrosion resistance.

BS EN 10025-6: 2019 + A1: 2022 Hot rolled products of structural steels. Technical delivery conditions for flat products of high yield strength structural steels in the quenched and tempered condition.

BS EN 10149-1: 2013 Hot rolled flat products made of high yield strength steels for cold forming. General technical delivery conditions.

BS EN 10149-2: 2013 Hot rolled flat products made of high yield strength steels for cold forming. Technical delivery conditions for thermo-mechanically rolled steel.

BS EN 10149-3: 2013 Hot rolled flat products made of high yield strength steels for cold forming. Technical delivery conditions for normalized or normalized rolled steels.

BS EN 10169: 2022 Continuously organic coated (coil coated) steel flat products. Technical delivery conditions.

BS EN 13170: 2012 + A2: 2018 Thermal insulation products for buildings. Factory made products of expanded cork (ICB). Specification.

BS EN 13501-1: 2018 Fire classification of construction products and building elements. Classification using data from reaction to fire tests.

BS EN 13984: 2013 Flexible sheets for waterproofing. Plastic and rubber vapour control layers. Definitions and characteristics.

BS EN 14080: 2013 Timber structures. Glued laminated timber and glued solid timber. Requirements.

BS EN 15804: 2012 + A2: 2019 Sustainability of construction works. Environmental product declarations. Core rules for the product category of construction products.

BS EN 15824: 2017 Specification for external renders and internal plasters based on organic binders.

BS EN ISO 1461: 2022 Hot dipped galvanized coatings on fabricated iron and steel articles. Specifications and test methods.

BS EN ISO 14001: 2015 Environmental management systems. Requirements with guidance for use.

PAS 24: 2022 Enhanced security performance requirements for doorsets and windows in the UK.

PAS 8820: 2016 Construction materials. Alkali-activated cementitious material and concrete. Specification.

BES 6001 Framework Standard for Responsible Sourcing. v. 4.0, 2022, British Standards Institution, London.

Building Research Establishment Publication

BREEAM UK New Construction, Version 6, Ref. SD5079, 24/08/2022, BRE Global, Watford.

BRE Home Quality Mark (HQM), Version 6, 6 July 2023, BRE Group, Watford.

BRE Information Papers

BRE IP 14/11 Hemp lime. *An introduction to low-impact building materials.* Sutton, A., Black, D. and Walker, P., IHS Press, Watford.

BRE IP 15/11 Straw bale. *An introduction to low-impact building materials.* Sutton, A., Black, D. and Walker, P., IHS Press, Watford.

BRE IP 16/11 Unfired clay masonry. *An introduction to low-impact building materials.* Sutton, A., Black, D. and Walker, P., IHS Press, Watford.

BRE IP 17/11 Cross-laminated timber. *An introduction to low-impact building materials:* Sutton, A., Black, D. and Walker, P., IHS Press, Watford.

BRE IP 18/11 Natural Fibre Insulation. *An Introduction to Low-impact Building Materials.* Sutton, A., Black, D. and Walker, P., IHS Press, Watford.

BM TRADA Wood Information Sheets

WIS 0-3, 2020, Introduction to timber frame construction. BM TRADA, High Wycombe.

WIS 1-6, 2016, Glued laminated timber. BM TRADA, High Wycombe.

WIS 2/3-59 2020 Recovering and minimising waste wood. BMTRADA, High Wycombe.

WIS 2/3-61, 2016 Cross laminated timber: Introduction for specifiers. BM TRADA, High Wycombe.

WIS 2/3-63 2021 Modified wood products. BM TRADA, High Wycombe.

WIS 2/3-72 2022 Carbon and timber in construction for building designers. BM TRADA, High Wycombe.

MPA The Concrete Centre

Offsite Concrete Construction. A guide to the design and construction of precast concrete in buildings, Ref. TCC/03/04, 2019, MPA The Concrete Centre, London.

Modern Methods of Construction. Concrete Quarterly, Autumn 2019, MPA The Concrete Centre, London.

Government Publications

DLUHC: Department for Levelling Up, Housing and Communities, UK Government Department.

Homes England: Non-departmental public body that funds affordable housing in England.

House of Lords Built Environment Committee, UK Government.

Circular Ecology

ICE: Inventory of Carbon and Energy, v. 3.0, 10 November 2019, Hammond, G. and Jones, C., University of Bath.

Index

9 781032 414829